Girls

£5.15

IDE

TIME TO TALK

TWELVE-YEAR-OLD Sarah Appleby was having problems with her homework.

I can't do this algebra. I'll ring Natalie and see how she's getting on with it.

Hi! Nat?

No. My name's Shirley.

Oh — sorry! I must have dialled the wrong number.

Don't worry. You sound about my age. I wonder if I know you. Do you live in Medenhampton? I live just outside town.

Yes — my name's Sarah. I go to Dales School.

Oh, yeah. I've heard of it. I go to St Anne's.

8

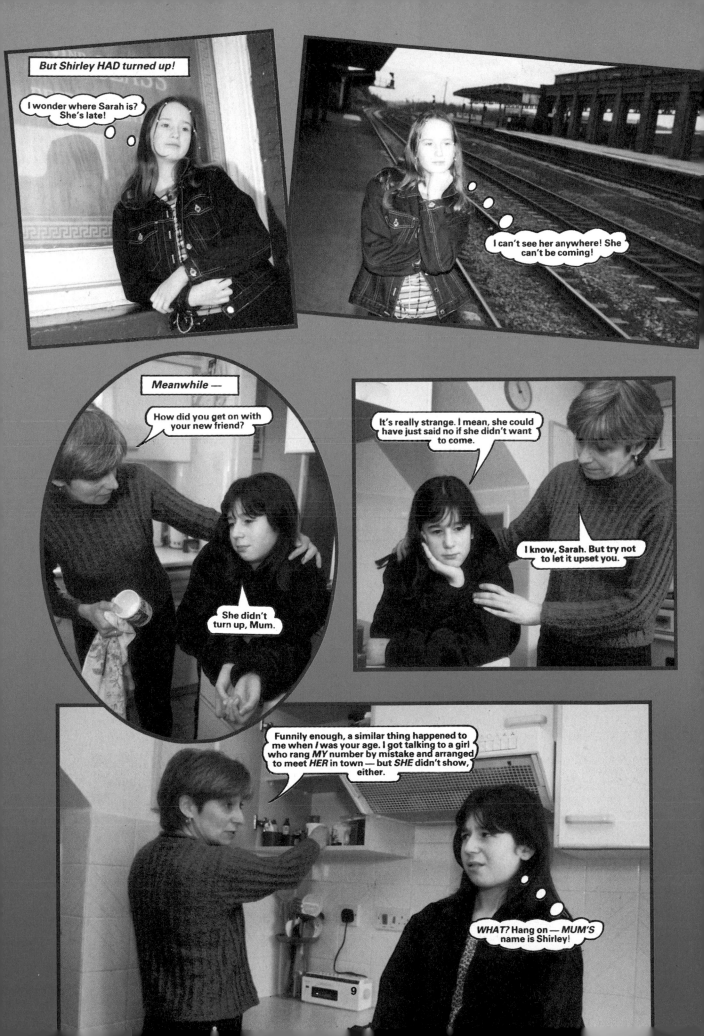

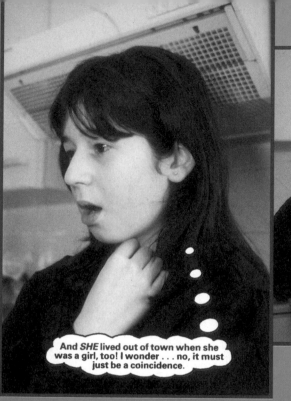

The End

EMMA BUNTON

IT'S A DATE!

JANUARY

S	3	10	17	24	31
M	4	11	18	25	—
Tu	5	12	19	26	—
W	6	13	20	27	—
Th	7	14	21	28	—
F	1	8	15	22	29
S	2	9	16	23	30	—

PETER ANDRE

IMPORTANT DATES!

A. J. McLean
(Backstreet Boys) — 9th

Glenn Clarke
(OTT) — 9th

Melanie Chisholm
(Spice Girls) — 11th

Crispian Mills
(lead singer, Kula Shaker)
— 18th

Gary Barlow — 20th

Easther Bennett
(Eternal) — 20th

Emma Bunton
(Spice Girls) — 21st

Mark Owen — 27th

Nick Carter
(Backstreet Boys) — 28th

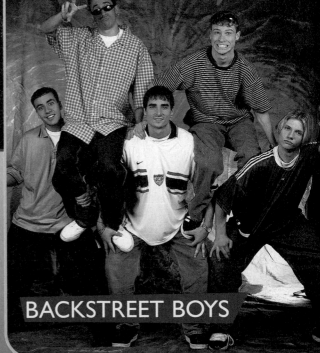

BACKSTREET BOYS

11

It's A Date!

FEBRUARY

S	–	7	14	21	28
M	1	8	15	22	–
Tu	2	9	16	23	–
W	3	10	17	24	–
Th	4	11	18	25	–
F	5	12	19	26	–
S	6	13	20	27	–

JENNIFER ANISTON

ROBBIE WILLIAMS

WRITE ON!

Zoë Ball
Syon Lodge
London Bridge
Isleworth
Middlesex
TW7 5BH

Gary Barlow
69-79 Bedford House
Fulham High Street
London
SW6 3JW

Baywatch
c/o 5433
Beethoven Street
Los Angeles
CA 90066 USA

Jamie Theakston
c/o The O-Zone
Room G7
99 Great Portland
Street
London WA1 1AA

IMPORTANT DATES!

Michelle Gayle — 2nd

Steve McManaman
(Liverpool F.C.) — 11th

Jennifer Aniston — 11th

Jesse Spencer
(Billy Kennedy in
"Neighbours") — 12th

Robbie Williams — 13th

Valentine's Day — 14th

Shrove Tuesday — 16th

Brian Litrell
(Backstreet Boys) — 20th

Peter Andre — 27th

MARCH

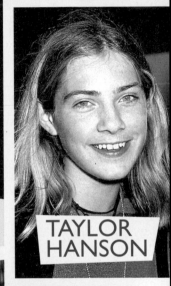

BOYZONE

S	–	7	14	21	28
M	1	8	15	22	29
Tu	2	9	16	23	30
W	3	10	17	24	31
Th	4	11	18	25	–
F	5	12	19	26	–
S	6	13	20	27	–

IMPORTANT DATES!

St David's Day — 1st

Jon Bon Jovi — 2nd

Ronan Keating (Boyzone) — 3rd

Patsy Kensit — 4th

Graham Coxon (Blur) — 12th

Kelle Bryan (Eternal) — 12th

Mother's Day — 14th

Taylor Hanson — 14th

St Patrick's Day — 17th

Stephen Gately (Boyzone) — 17th

Mark Hamilton (Ash) — 21st

Damon Albarn (Blur) — 23rd

Melanie Blatt (All Saints) — 25th

Mariah Carey — 27th

Clocks go forward — 28th

WRITE ON!

Blur
P.O. Box 525
Stoke-on-Trent
ST7 2YX

Bon Jovi
P.O. Box 326
Fords
New Jersey
NY 08863 USA

Boyzone
P.O. Box 102
Stanmore
Middlesex
HA7 2PY

Robbie Williams
P.O. Box 479
Newcastle-Under-
Lyme ST5 1BP

TAYLOR HANSON

BLUR

Make 'n'

FURRY FUN

Turn a Dullsville old cork pin-board into something dazzling in next to no time. You can even give it a different look on each side and change around when you feel like it. It's easy-peasy — here's how.

We'll start with the WRONG side of the pin-board. (The one that isn't cork.)

What you need:
Coloured drawing pins
Piece of fur fabric
Narrow ribbon or bias binding (from fabric shops)
Glue
Felt

What to do:
1. Measure the size of the area inside the pin-board frame.
2. Cut out a piece of fur fabric that's the same size.
3. Glue the fabric to the board and leave to dry.
4. Cut 13 shapes from felt. We used a daisy shape, but stars, circles or triangles would also look good. If you want to use a daisy or a star, you can trace round our template and cut a pattern from paper.
5. Now add the ribbon or binding .
Start with 2 long pieces going from corner to corner. Put a felt shape over the ribbon at each corner and then secure them with drawing pins. Add another shape and drawing pin where the 2 ribbons cross in the middle. Measure along each side and put a small pencil mark at the halfway points.

Cut 4 shorter pieces of ribbon to put on to make a diamond shape. Secure with shapes and pins. Add more shapes and pins where the ribbons cross. You can use the pins to hold important notes in place or just slide things behind the binding.

DO

FLOWER POWER

What you need:
Small amount of paint
Scraps of flower patterned fabric or wrapping paper
Glue
Ribbon and drawing pins as before

What to do:
1. Paint the wooden frame of the pin-board and leave to dry.
2. Make a watery mix of paint by adding about a cup full of water to 2 teaspoons of paint. Paint the cork area with this mixture (this is called a wash) and leave to dry. You may need to add another coat as the cork soaks up a lot of paint!
3. Carefully cut some of the flower shapes out of the fabric or paper. Glue these onto the pin board.
4. Add your ribbon or binding and drawing pins as before. Cool!

TEMPLATE FOR STAR

TEMPLATE FOR FLOWER

Wildlife
KOALA AND BABY

playing the part

Today's the big day, Kelly — I wonder if Mrs Jones will let you go ahead with your musical project.

I hope so. I'm dead nervous, Danni.

Then —

Hi, babes.

Did you hear anything, Danni?

No, Kelly.

It must have been my imagination. It sounded like an apeman. Mind you, I *DID* dream about a gorilla last night.

Do you think you should have been so rude to Liam, Kel?

It's time someone took him down a peg or two. He's too full of himself.

But why did it have to be me? Liam and his gang are a right bunch of toughs. I don't know what came over me.

But, by lunchtime, Kelly had better things to think about —

I've read your script, Kelly, and yes, I don't see why the drama club can't put it on.

That's brilliant, Mrs Jones. Thanks.

17

What about the music for the songs, Kelly?

Joe is going to do that. Mr Hilditch, his music teacher, said he'd help.

Well, you'll have to get on with it. I want to hold auditions next week.

Sure, miss. I've done some work on it already.

Kelly went to Joe's after school —

How about this for the opening song?

Yeah, great. That's really catchy.

Joe's brilliant. I'm glad he's my boyfriend.

Later, at the pictures —

I got through loads of stuff for the play, there. We make a good team, eh, Kel?

Yeah. I'm sure our musical will be a success.

Then —

I've told you lot before, you're banned!

Yeah, yeah! Okay, Grandad, we're going.

Typical — Liam and his gang causing trouble!

Liam's such a loser.

Yeah. Still, let's forget him — the film'll be starting soon.

Next week, at the auditions —

Joe's doing well in the lead male role. It'd be great if we could both get the main parts. After all, we have written most of this together.

Then —

Yes, Liam? Have you come to audition?

Huh! Cause trouble more like. What does *HE* want?

18

Make way, Joey boy, for someone who *KNOWS* what he's doing!

That'll be right — he'll be hopeless!

But —

Hmm. Liam's very good, isn't he, Kelly?

I don't believe it! He *IS*!

Thank you all for coming. I'll do my selection tonight and put up a list tomorrow.

Well, there's no contest as to who's gonna get the lead part, eh? I was brilliant!

Oh, sure! She won't pick *YOU*, Liam. She needs someone who's reliable.

Yeah. You've *NO* chance!

But, on the way home —

You don't think Mrs Jones *WILL* pick Liam do you, Mum?

I don't know, love. If he's the best for the part, then yes, she might.

But I wrote that part with Joe in mind. If Liam gets it, the whole thing will be ruined. Mrs Jones *CAN'T* pick him!

But, next day —

Oh, no! Liam *DID* get the lead!

I spy a sad loser. Told you I'd get it, didn't I? See ya in rehearsals, Kel!

He's gross! And as I've got the lead female part, I'm gonna be spending a lot of time with him. *YEUK!*

19

CONTINUED ON PAGE 30.

tv teasers!

what's on?

Read the clues below and guess which TV prog we're describing!

1) It's double trouble when you find your twin sister after being separated at birth.
2) Wow, Johnny and Denise must get up mega-early to go to work.
3) Mulder and Scully are always off investigating the paranormal.
4) 3 boys, 3 girls, living in New York, hanging out in the local coffee house and having loads of laughs!
5) They're the best of friends. They both work in the same shop and one of them loves orange soda!

music box!

We've scrambled up the names of well-known music programmes. Can you unscramble them and then answer the questions?

1) FOOT STEP HOPP.
2) TONE HOZE.
3) SHOWER THATCH.

A) Who presents music programme number 2?
B) Who co-presents with her?
C) Which show does he also present?

odd one out

Can you guess which person or programme shouldn't be in each of the lists below?

1) *Uh-oh! One of the girls isn't a Byker Grove babe. Who is it?*
KAREN, BEVERLY, SITA, BRIGID, CHER.
2) *Which of these people isn't a talk show host?*
RICKI LAKE, VANESSA FELTZ, VIC REEVES, OPRAH WINFREY, JERRY SPRINGER.
3) *All of these programmes are American sitcoms, or are they?*
FRIENDS, ROSEANNE, FRESH PRINCE OF BEL AIR, FATHER TED, BOY MEETS WORLD.
4) *One of these programmes isn't set in the north of England.*
CORONATION STREET, EMMERDALE, THE BILL, HOLLYOAKS, BROOKSIDE.
5) *Which of these people has never appeared in EastEnders?*
MICHELLE GAYLE, SEAN MAGUIRE, DANIELLA WESTBROOK, NICK BERRY, WILL MELLOR.

20

crossed out!

Fill in the answers to these soap clues to reveal this TV hunk's character in the shaded area!

1) He was Claire's step-dad in EastEnders.
2) Neighbours' Madge and Harold's "religious" surname.
3) Where Hollyoaks is set!
4) Mr and Mrs Benson's eldest son.
5) Grant, Peggy and Phil.
6) Mandy, Zak, Lisa, Sam, Butch and Marlon – Emmerdale's zany family!
7) She's Darren's girlfriend, Karl and Susan's daughter and Billy and Mal's sister!
8) Home And Away's seasonal Bay.
9) "Not straight" Mr Watts who runs Firmans Freezer Centre and was married to Raquel.
10) She left the Bay last year to join Shannon in Paris.
11) The younger Battersby daughter who sometimes works in Roy and Gail's café.

match the man

*You may know their characters' names but what are their **real** names? Match each actor to his character and then to the show he appears in!*

MATTHEW PERRY
MARTIN CLUNES
ROSS KEMP
BEN FREEMAN
JOHNNY GALECKI

GRANT
DAVID
CHRIS
CHANDLER
GARY

ROSEANNE
GRANGE HILL
FRIENDS
MEN BEHAVING BADLY
EASTENDERS

tv dinners

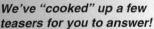

We've "cooked" up a few teasers for you to answer!

1) Can you name the TV chef shown below?
2) Name three cooking programmes he has appeared in!
3) Which cookery show is presented by a lady named Fern Britton?

21

I *KNOW* that scenery flat was secure earlier. I can't think how it came untied.

It must have been untied deliberately. But who would do it? and *WHY?*

Later — That didn't go too well, I'm afraid. The scenery fall seemed to have upset everybody. We'll finish early.

I'm glad. That gave me quite a scare. It's almost as if it was *MEANT* to hit me.

That must have been awful for you, Louise.

Yeah, terrible! Mustn't have the *STAR* upset, *MUST* we?

At the café — Why's he looking at you like that, Louise?

That's Alan. I used to go out with him.

HE could have interfered with the scenery. Or it could have been Tracy — she was annoyed with me. Maybe I'm just being silly . . .

Next time — No lights now? What on earth's going on? I'm wondering if it's worth all this effort. I'm tempted to cancel the production.

Oh, but that would upset Louise. And just think about all the attention she's got with all these things going wrong.

But, after a few more rehearsals — Very good, everyone! Everything seems to have gone more smoothly for the last few rehearsals.

I'd still like to know who was responsible, though, and why? They still might have something else planned.

Funny how everything went okay when the production was threatened. I bet YOU did all those things, course.

Yes, you enjoyed getting all the attention, but had to stop when you thought the play was at risk.

WHAT? That's not true!

Next day —

I can't remember my lines. Everybody thinks I caused that trouble and I can't think about anything else now.

Wake up, Louise! This is no time to start forgetting your lines.

And —

Louise, you're supposed to come on now. You're missing your cues. I'm telling you, I'd cancel rather than put on a poor show. It would spoil our reputation.

Next rehearsal —

I must concentrate. The last thing I want is to have the play cancelled because of me. Oh, yuk! There's something sticky in this bag, but I won't let on. Now I KNOW somebody's getting at me.

Afterwards —

. . . and it made my hand really sticky, but I didn't let on. I wouldn't let whoever it was . . . oh, why didn't I think of it before? I bet it's Penny who's been causing all this trouble.

PENNY? Hm, you're probably right, Louise.

When Louise arrived home —

I've got all this stuff to sort for my fund-raising, Louise. Want to help?

Sure, Mum.

This dress has just given me an idea how I might trap Penny. I'll go round to Clare's afterwards and tell her about it.

But, later —

Clare's in the bath so I can't tell her now. Never mind, it might be best if I keep my idea to myself anyway, just in case Clare accidentally gives it away.

So —

... and I thought it would be good for the third scene.

Lovely, Louise. Yes, it will do nicely. Go and put it in the costumes room.

I'm sure you'll look absolutely *WONDERFUL* in it!

Penny's got a couple of minutes free in scene two and nobody'll miss her. She won't be able to stop herself from spoiling *THIS*. But *I'M* free too, so I'll catch her out if she does.

And, a little later —

I *KNEW* it! Thank goodness it was only a dress from the jumble.

Caught you! Oh! *CLARE!* But *WHY?*

Because you're so *PERFECT!* You have *EVERYTHING* — nice home, lots of things, and you're the star of the show. You think you're so much better than me and it makes me sick! Why shouldn't you have a bad time for a change?

There was never any need for you to be jealous and as for the rest of what you said, well, that's all in your own mind. Now, I think I'd better go and explain things to Sarah and the rest, *DON'T YOU?*

Clare was asked to leave. At the play's first night —

A special round of applause, please, for our star, Louise Grant.

It's sad that Clare had to act the way she did, but at least the play was a great success.

THE END

THE WHITE LADY

FIONA and Clare were sitting on the bench by the netball courts, watching the school team's lunchtime practice session, when Clare's twin sister, Sally, came running over to them.

"Guess what?" she grinned, as she pushed between them, wriggling to make space. "Victoria Wilson's invited us to her Hallowe'en party next Friday!"

"*Wow!*" cried Clare. "She lives in Grave's End, that big, old house by the cemetery. What a brilliant place for a Hallowe'en party."

"I've heard that it's supposed to be haunted," said Fiona.

Sally scoffed. "People *always* say that about big, old houses. Victoria's never said anything about any ghost."

"Yes, but they've only lived there for a few months," said Fiona. "So this will be their first Hallowe'en there. *Wahahaa!*"

Sally and Clare laughed and dodged as Fiona raised her arms and stretched her fingers, stabbing the air spookily.

"I've heard the ghost is supposed to be a white lady," Fiona said as the three girls walked into school.

"Isn't it always? Whenever there's a ghost *somebody's* bound to mention a white lady," Clare laughed. "The ghost world must be *full* of them!"

"Anyway," said Sally, "about the party.

Victoria says it's fancy dress. I think I'll go as a witch."

"Me, too," said Clare. "We can be *twin* witches! How about you, Fiona?"

"Not me," she replied. "I'll go as something else." And she smiled secretively.

No matter how much they pestered her, she wouldn't tell. All she would say was "Wait and see".

* * * *

On the night of the party, Sally and Clare were ready first. They wore boots, long skirts and capes, with plastic pointed hats and hooked noses from the toy shop. Their dad had made them broomsticks from old poles and twigs.

"Okay, sis," said Sally. "Let's go and meet Fiona and see what *her* outfit is!"

The two girls gasped when they saw their friend.

"The White Lady!" said Sally. "We should have guessed."

Fiona was wearing a flowing white dress and had a sheet of white netting, veiling her face. Clare leaned towards her, peering closely through the veil.

"We can't see your face," she said.

"That's the idea," replied Fiona. "I can see you, though. Look!"

As she lifted the veil they saw she had coated her hands with white make-up and the veins were picked out in blue eye pencil. They looked weird, mottled like old marble. The girls shrieked as the veil went back even further, because Fiona's face was made-up to match her hands. She looked really ghostly.

"See?" she said. "You can't see my face because it's the same colour as the veil, but *I* can see everything!"

"It's brilliant, Fiona," said Clare. "Dead spooky!"

* * * *

Fiona's dad gave them a lift round to Victoria's house. As they drove up they could see the outside lighting was purple, making everything look sinister. Sally shivered, excited at the thought of the party ahead. Inside the light was dim, mainly lit with candles in pumpkins. The hall had huge strings of cobwebs that brushed against their faces and big black plastic spiders and bats hung in the air.

The girls stared round in amazement. As they expected, there were lots of witches, a few vampires, the odd Dracula or two, a skeleton and a Morticia Addams. But there was only one White Lady. Everybody thought Fiona's costume was fantastic.

. . . spiders and bats hung in the air.

"Well done, Fee," said Victoria. "You're the only original one here tonight."

"Is she smiling?" asked Clare. "It's weird not seeing you, Fiona."

In reply, Fiona made a gliding movement round them, brushing against them softly with her fingers. Everybody around them laughed.

"Help yourself to food and drink," called Victoria. "It's in the kitchen."

They went to see. There was a huge black cauldron in the middle of the table, full of fruit juice. Plates piled high with food were all around and Victoria's mum had made pumpkin pie.

"This is some party," said Sally. "Let's go and dance for a bit. We can get some food later."

It was fun dancing, though the twins' hats kept wobbling, but it was even better watching the others. They giggled as they watched the skeleton dancing with a vampire, and a Dracula obviously

fancied one of the witches.

"There's so much black here," said Clare. "Your costume really stands out, Fiona."

"Thanks," she cried above the music. "Look, I'll go and get us some food and drink. You keep these places and I'll bring some on a tray."

However, a few moments later, she was back.

"Hey, where's the food, Fiona?" asked Sally.

Fiona just leaned towards them, beckoning spookily with her white, bony hands. She was moving to the music, very strangely.

Clare and Sally laughed.

"You're getting into the spirit of things, Fiona," said Clare. "Get it, Sally? The *spirit* of things. Ha! Ha! "

Fiona stopped and stared at them. At least, it looked as if she was staring — they couldn't really tell.

"You're acting dead spooky, Fiona," chuckled Clare. "You'll scare us for real if you're not careful."

...beckoning spookily with her white, bony hands.

Fiona beckoned, moving slowly backwards, and the two girls giggled as they followed.

They went through the main hall into a tiny passageway.

"Hey, are you sure it's okay to come down here, Fiona? I mean, there's nobody else around," Sally asked.

But Clare grinned.

"She's just playing the part, Sal. Let's go along with it for a laugh."

Just then there was a loud crash and they turned to see sausage rolls and crisps scattered on the hall floor at the end of the corridor. Fruit juice was flowing around the food.

"*Oops!* Somebody's dropped a tray," said Clare.

"Oh, what a mess!" came a voice from the hall.

"That voice sounds just like you, Fiona," said Clare as she turned back. But Fiona was nowhere to be seen.

"Where's she gone?" wondered Sally.

"Through there, I suppose," said Clare, pointing to the only door in front of them.

"Come on, Fiona, we know where you're hiding," called Sally as she opened the door.

But the little room was empty apart from a few cardboard boxes.

"I don't get it," said Clare. "She *was* here."

But, as they turned back to look towards the hall, they could see somebody was picking up the spilled food. Someone dressed in white. Fiona!

She looked up as Clare and Sally walked slowly towards her.

"Sorry, you two, I dropped the eats. Anyway, what're you doing here? Thought you were keeping the seats?"

Clare turned to Sally, her hand trembling as she pointed to Fiona. Both girls were pale-faced and shaking.

Fiona laughed.

"Okay, I know I'm spooky, but there's no need to go over the top. You've got used to me now. Help me clear this lot up."

"You're Fi . . . Fiona," Clare gibbered.

"Sure am," said Fiona. "I'm not really the White Lady, you know. Just pretending."

"We thought we were following *you* down here. We followed a white lady, then she disappeared into thin air!"

Fiona froze as she picked up a battered sausage roll.

"What? You mean . . ."

"Y-yes," stammered Clare. "If *you're* Fiona and *you've* just been in the kitchen, then *who* were we following?"

The End

29

playing the part

CONTINUED FROM PAGE 19.

I can't believe Mrs Jones! Liam is the *LAST* person we wanted in the show. He's just trouble!

I know. It's the pits!

Though Liam *DID* do a good audition.

I'm sure Liam'll mess up, though. He'll soon get bored. You wait, Joe, I bet he doesn't even show for the first rehearsal.

I hope you're right, Kelly. Then Mrs Jones can choose someone reliable instead.

Joe's dead disappointed about not getting the part. But I want what's best for the show and Liam *WAS* the best. Mind you, I don't know if I fancy acting opposite him.

Next day, at school —

Hi, Kelly. How's my new girlfriend looking forward to the rehearsal tonight?

Hey! Who d'you think you're talking to, Liam? Kelly's *MY* girlfriend!

Yeah, yeah. Keep your hair on, Joey boy.

Well, just remember, Kelly's *NOT* your girlfriend.

Kelly? Why didn't *YOU* say something to Liam? I don't want him calling you his girlfriend.

He only meant I'm his girlfriend in the show, Joe. Don't let him get to you.

30

I don't want to upset Liam. He's got a real temper and could ruin everything.

At the first rehearsal —

Ah, Kelly, come on in. We've been waiting for you.

Oh! Liam's here already. And there's me thinking he wouldn't even bother to turn up.

But, then —

What are you lot doing here? I don't remember you being cast in any parts.

We've come to support Liam, miss.

Well, I don't think he needs your support. Please leave!

Yeah, gimme a break, guys. I'll catch you later.

That had better not happen again, Liam.

It won't, miss. I promise.

Liam reads the part really well. But I still don't think he'll stick it out. Either he or his mates will mess up soon.

Soon —

Wouldn't it be more in character if I just say 'okay' here rather than all this unnecessary stuff?

Yes, Liam, I think that would be an improvement. We'll do that bit again.

31

After the rehearsal —

Huh! HE'S got a nerve suggesting changes to the script, when the highest grade he's ever got in English is a D.

Yeah, I know, Joe.

But it WAS an improvement. And Liam was really easy to act with. I can hardly believe it.

Joe stayed to tea —

I've got some things I have to do before I can give you a lift home, Joe. Why don't you and Kelly run through your lines?

Yeah, good idea, Mum.

So —

Your cue is, 'Hey, hang about!'.

I hate to think it, but Liam reads the part better than Joe. Maybe Mrs Jones hasn't made a mistake after all.

But Kelly still didn't trust Liam —

There he is, acting up as usual. I wonder why he *REALLY* wants to do this play? What if he's planning to trash it?

Kelly asked her mum —

Maybe he's just found something he likes and he's good at it. Don't worry, love. I'm sure things'll work out fine.

Yeah, I'm sure you're right, Mum.

But, the next day —

That's enough, Liam Brown! Get outside! I won't tolerate your disruptive behaviour in my class a moment longer!

No sweat. I'm on my way.

At break —

Liam was a real pain today. I don't know how you can put up with him in the show.

He's not like that when we're acting together, Danni. He's different.

Ooh, *DIFFERENT*, is he? You sound as though you're starting to fancy him.

WHAT? NO WAY!

But, come to think of it, the Liam I know on stage could be very fanciable indeed.

CONTINUED ON PAGE 49.

32

KRYSTAL MASON and her family had just moved to a new town, and Krystal was about to start a new school. The trouble was, Krystal had a secret —

You two had better get a move on! You don't want to be late on your first day, do you?

No, Mum.

I'm really dreading this — I hope no-one guesses my secret!

KRYSTAL CLEAR

At school —

Good, there's a seat free at the front. I'll just sit there.

But —

Sorry, you can't sit there — it's Suzi's!

Oh, no! This is awful. Everyone's looking!

But Krystal was spotted —

At lunchtime —

That weekend, at a Christmas Fair —

How much are these bath salts, please?

I'll be with you in a sec.

They're one pound fifty.

OH! She — she's BLIND!

Break time, Nicole! I'll take over now.

Thanks for asking me to help out today, Mrs Hanson. I'm really enjoying myself!

Nicole's such a brave girl! Not one word of self-pity have I heard from her since she was blinded in an accident last year!

Afterwards —

That poor girl. I've been so silly! I'm going to ask Mum to make an appointment at the optician's for me as soon as I get home.

So, on Monday —

Try these on, Krystal.

I suppose they're not too bad.

36

37

THE END

penny's place

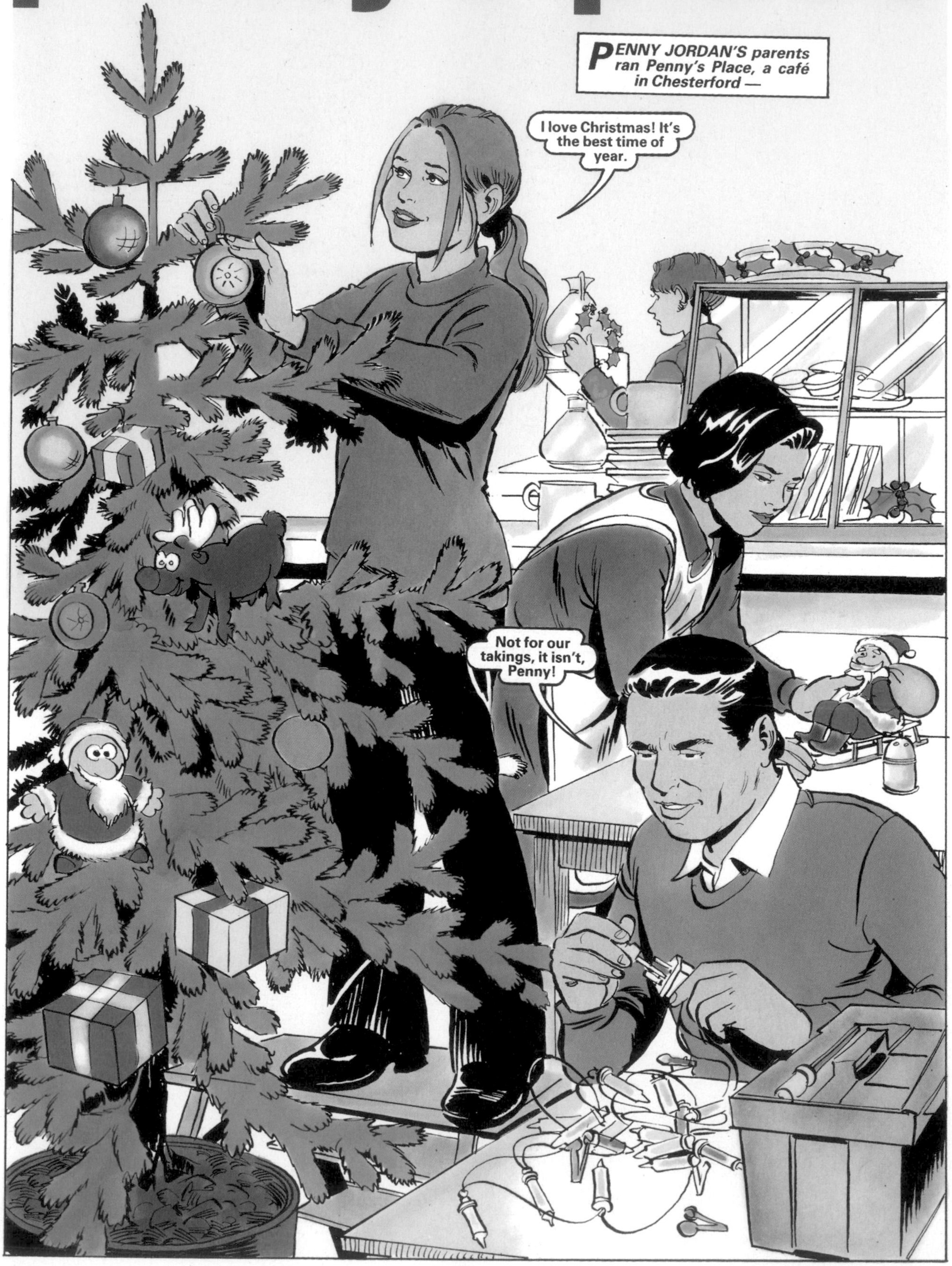

Oh, there's the bell for next period. Hurry up or we'll be late!

After school —

We'd better get the food set out!

OH! Penny — LOOK!

And, inside —

OH, NO!

The whole place is flooded. It's a disaster!

Some idiot left the tap running in here, that's why!

Come on, Max. Let's get out of here . . .

Yeah. It wasn't OUR fault. And WHO wants to go to a stupid disco, anyway?

Hmm . . . I wonder why Fran and Maxine are creeping off.

42

43

THE END

44

It's A Date!

APRIL

VICTORIA ADAMS

IMPORTANT DATES!

April Fool's Day — *1st*
Chris Evans — *1st*
Good Friday — *2nd*
Easter Sunday — *4th*
Easter Monday — *5th*
Claire Danes — *12th*
Paul Nicholls — *12th*
Sean Maguire — *16th*
Victoria Adams
(Spice Girls) — *17th*
St George's Day — *21st*

S	—	4	11	18	25
M	—	5	12	19	26
Tu	—	6	13	20	27
W	—	7	14	21	28
Th	1	8	15	22	29
F	2	9	16	23	30
S	3	10	17	24	—

WRITE ON!

Brookside
Productions Campus
Abbey Road
Liverpool
L16 0JP

Coronation Street
c/o Granada TV
Quay Street
Manchester
M60 9EA

Leonardo DiCaprio
c/o CAA
9830 Wilshire
Boulevard
Beverly Hills
CA 90212
USA

911
P.O. Box 911
Glasgow
G1 3PQ

911

It's A Date!

MAY

S	2	9	16	23	30
M	3	10	17	24	31
Tu	4	11	18	25	–
W	5	12	19	26	–
Th	6	13	20	27	–
F	7	14	21	28	–
S	1	8	15	22	29	–

JANET JACKSON

MELANIE BROWN

IMPORTANT DATES!

May Day Holiday — *3rd*
George Clooney — *6th*
Dave Rowntree
(Blur) — *8th*
Harry Enfield — *11th*
Natalie Appleton
(All Saints) — *14th*
Janet Jackson — *16th*

Vernie Bennet
(Eternal) — *17th*
Kylie Minogue — *28th*
Noel Gallagher
(Oasis) — *29th*
Melanie Brown
(Spice Girls) — *29th*
Start of Spring — *31st*

WRITE ON!

ER
c/o Amblin
Entertainment
100 Universal Plaza
Bungalow
477 Universal City
CA 91608
USA

Chris Evans
Ginger Production
Media Centre
131-151 Great
Titchfield Street
London
W1P

3T
P.O. Box 11234
Elkins Park
PA 110271234
USA

Friends
c/o 400 Warner
Boulevard
Burbank
CA 91522
USA

IMPORTANT DATES!

Alanis Morissette — 1st
Scott Wolf
(Party Of Five) — 4th
Mark Wahlberg — 5th
The Artist (Formerly Known
As Prince) — 7th
Courteney Cox
(Friends) — 15th
Nicole Kidman — 20th
Father's Day — 20th
Jamie Redknapp
(Liverpool F.C.) — 25th
George Michael — 25th

WRITE ON!

**Home And Away
Merchandise
Service**
P.O. Box 406
Beaconsfield
Bucks
HP9 2HQ

Gina G
28 Kensington
Church Street
London
W8 4EG

Ryan Giggs
c/o Manchester
United F.C.
Old Trafford
Manchester
M16 0RA

Neighbours
Grundy Television
448 Pacific Highway
Artamon
NSW 2009
Australia

COURTENEY COX

GINA G

JAMIE REDKNAPP

JUNE

S	–	6	13	20	27
M	–	7	14	21	28
Tu	1	8	15	22	29
W	2	9	16	23	30
Th	3	10	17	24	–
F	4	11	18	25	–
S	5	12	19	26	–

Wildlife
CHIMPANZEE

playing the part

CONTINUED FROM PAGE 32.

I can't really fancy Liam, can I? He's total trouble. But he's so nice on stage — what if *THAT'S* the real Liam and the bully boy stuff is an act?

Nope — no way! Wise up, Kel! Why am I worried about Liam when I've got Joe for a boyfriend? He's great.

Kelly and Joe went bowling —

Aw! *ANOTHER* gutter ball!

Not your night, is it, Joe? I'm well ahead in the scoring!

Then —

Oh! That boy — for a minute I thought he was Liam.

I bet Liam's really good at bowling. Not like Joe — he's just scored another zero.

The Liam look-alike and his girlfriend are having so much fun. I'm just dead embarrassed because Joe is so naff at this.

You okay, Kelly? You look miles away.

49

Afterwards —

Come on, Joe — our time's up!

Okay, okay. What's the rush?

What's up, Kel? You've hardly said a word since we left the bowling alley. Have I done something wrong?

Er — no. I've just got a bit of a headache, that's all. Look, I'll phone you tomorrow, okay?

But, the next day —

I don't know what's the matter with me. I can't be bothered ringing Joe. I think I'll give it a miss. I'll see him at school tomorrow, anyway.

But, at school —

Hi, Kelly. I've been looking for you.

It's Liam!

I wondered if we could meet at lunchtime? I've got an idea for the musical I'd like to go over. Maybe we could meet in the music room?

Sure, I'll be there. One o'clock, okay?

Liam was dead nice. When his stupid mates aren't around, he's totally different. And I can't believe how much I'm looking forward to meeting him.

Later, in class —

Do concentrate on the matter in hand, Kelly, or you might set the school on fire!

Eh? Oh yes, sir. Sorry, sir.

I was miles away thinking about Liam then. I wish it was lunchtime already.

50

At last —

Thanks for coming, Kelly. I've — er — rewritten the melody of the song we do together. I think I've improved it.

Yeah?

He CAN'T have! Liam's always bottom of the class in everything. He's totally stupid!

But —

It's brilliant! MUCH better than the melody Joe wrote for the song. Joe'll go spare!

But, then —

Hiya, Liam. We've been looking for you. What're you up to?

Oh, no! Liam's yobby mates!

Leave it out, lads. I'm busy.

Don't mind us. We'll just practise our Oasis impression.

Cool it! I need some peace!

Yikes! What a racket! They've spoiled everything!

And then —

What's this? What's going on, Brown? Leave those instruments alone.

Oh, no! Mr Hilditch!

You've no business in here, any of you! You'll ALL take a detention after school tomorrow!

What? But it's a rehearsal night. We CAN'T miss that!

51

CONTINUED ON PAGE 62.

Happy New

ARIES
(Mar 22-Apr 20)

NEW YEAR
It's all going to be happening for you! A few new friends look likely in the first half of the year and, although a pal may move away later, you'll manage to keep in touch.

NEW YOU
You're prone to impatience, but you should begin to grow out of that this year. Friends will love your sense of fun where school projects are concerned.

LOOK FORWARD TO:
Summer outings.
An exciting family event.
Possible romance in May.

WATCH OUT FOR:
A busy spell in autumn.
Carelessness.
Jealous people.

GEMINI
(May 22-June 21)

NEW YEAR
After a slow start, your feet may not touch the ground for quite a few months. You'll be the centre of attention at school for a week or two, when a competition result is known.

NEW YOU
Everyone's friend, that should be you — keeping folk amused with all the latest jokes and news! Just try not to be *too* inquisitive when a friend seems a bit quiet.

LOOK FORWARD TO:
Great news from abroad.
A hip new hobby.
Holiday romance.

WATCH OUT FOR:
Forgetful friends.
Undeserved criticism.
Summer cash shortage.

LEO
(July 24-Aug 23)

NEW YEAR
You'll make a major change in your life when a friend shares her good idea with you. School's full of intrigue and excitement when a new arrival is announced — *wow!*

NEW YOU
Your generous nature could leave you short of cash if you're not too careful, but friends should step forward to help you out. Try not to show off, when things go well.

LOOK FORWARD TO:
Fab fun this summer.
Changes in your appearance.
Concert news.

WATCH OUT FOR:
A super-strict teacher.
Forgetfulness.
Delays in making plans.

TAURUS
(Apr 21-May 21)

NEW YEAR
You'll achieve something important by the middle of the year, and could take up a new sport or hobby. Mum or Dad may need your help to plan an extra-special surprise.

NEW YOU
Your patience should be rewarded at home and school, as you take the time to listen to people and think before you act. Tempted to be bossy? Think again!

LOOK FORWARD TO:
Extra cash in spring.
Making new friends.
A surprise party.

WATCH OUT FOR:
Delays when travelling.
A friend who needs to talk.
Pocket money problems.

CANCER
(June 22-July 23)

NEW YEAR
Looking for a change? There should be quite a few new faces and things to try coming your way — especially around autumn. Sharing a secret may be a good move.

NEW YOU
You'll need your good memory to keep up with all that's planned this year. Try to enjoy what *you* have, and not be quite so envious of other people, though.

LOOK FORWARD TO:
Unexpected help at school!
Special celebrations!
A new arrival in your neighbourhood.

WATCH OUT FOR:
Hold ups on holiday.
Easter expense.
A school busybody.

VIRGO
(Aug 24-Sept 23)

NEW YEAR
A disappointment early on may make you think it's not going to be a good year, but you couldn't be more wrong. Almost everything you attempt should turn out well.

NEW YOU
It'll be hard not to criticise a friend who does something you don't like but, when you think about it, you may change your mind. You'll still be as organised as ever.

LOOK FORWARD TO:
An autumn trip.
The chance to meet a star!
Unexpected compliments.

WATCH OUT FOR:
Nosy new neighbours.
A friend with a problem.
Ways to help at home.

You! A new year — a new you? The answer's in the stars!

LIBRA
(Sept 24-Oct 23)

NEW YEAR
You'll give someone an excellent piece of advice early in the year, and receive your reward a few months later. Travel looks likely for you and a few of your best friends.

NEW YOU
More friends should be heading your way, because you're so nice to know. You'll have to move fast when a trip's being planned or your indecision could make you miss out.

LOOK FORWARD TO:
A chance to shine at school.
Praise from someone unexpected.
Exciting holiday news.

WATCH OUT FOR:
Gossip that's not true.
A friend leaving your area.
Unannounced arrivals.

SAGITTARIUS
(Nov 23-Dec 22)

NEW YEAR
Your year starts off busy and it'll be a while before things calm down. During the busy spell, you'll travel more than usual and take up a few new and exciting interests.

NEW YOU
You'll worry about not working hard enough early in the year, but things should work out fine. Suspicious moves may arouse your curiosity and you could find out a few fab facts.

LOOK FORWARD TO:
A new arrival in your family.
Extra responsibility at school.
More money in December.

WATCH OUT FOR:
Someone who needs your advice.
Being misunderstood.
A jealous neighbour.

AQUARIUS
(Jan 22-Feb 19)

NEW YEAR
You're set to meet a very exciting person early in the year and, although friends could be jealous at first, they'll be pleased for you. Family plans will feature strongly this spring.

NEW YOU
Good ideas should come your way quickly and easily, but you'll still annoy friends with your stubborn streak. You may get round to being less untidy but, then again, maybe not!

LOOK FORWARD TO:
Winter parties!
An interesting move.
Making your dreams come true!

WATCH OUT FOR:
Something taking ages to organise.
A bad-tempered boy.
Chances to help friends.

SCORPIO
(Oct 24-Nov 22)

NEW YEAR
School will be the source of quite a few changes this year — and you'll be happy about nearly *all* of them. You could also go on the holiday of a lifetime.

NEW YOU
You may be suspicious of someone who will seem to be stepping on your toes — you don't like not being in control. But it's a year to be strong — and to have lots of fun.

LOOK FORWARD TO:
Special family treats.
Autumn outings.
Making a great new friend.

WATCH OUT FOR:
Someone who's out to cause trouble.
Delays on a day out.
Competition at school.

CAPRICORN
(Dec 23-Jan 21)

NEW YEAR
A new arrival may occur in your family, neighbourhood or school, and be responsible for quite a few changes in your life. You'll achieve something you've always wanted.

NEW YOU
Normally easily embarrassed, your practical nature will see you through any difficult spells. You'll be less cautious when attempting new things and ready to take on a bit of responsibility.

LOOK FORWARD TO:
A special celebration.
Praise for giving good advice.
Laughter this spring.

WATCH OUT FOR:
Gossip within your family.
Heaps of homework.
Stepping on someone's toes.

PISCES
(Feb 20-Mar 21)

NEW YEAR
Major moves could take place in the summer for you or a close relative. At first you might feel disappointed about this, but you'll quickly see lots of plus points.

NEW YOU
Head in the clouds, that'll be you for the second half of the year. An idea that *sounds* good will need lots of work to get it off the ground, and you'll probably decide it's worth it.

LOOK FORWARD TO:
Happy holiday memories.
Learning new things.
A friend's new romance.

WATCH OUT FOR:
Hidden expense on a trip.
A bully at school.
Strange news.

drummer boy

LIZ, Mei and Kerry watched glumly as their headmistress, Mrs Simpkins, pinned yet another notice on the board.

It's a talent competition and look at the prizes. Think what we could do with two hundred and fifty pounds! We should enter. You never know — we could be the new Spice Girls.

Yeah. With our musical talent and your great voice, we'd be bound to win, Kerry.

You could be right. But we haven't got a drummer, not since Jess went to Cornvale High.

We could advertise in the school mag.

Yeah, Girls, Girls, Girls. In need of a drummer. Auditions in the gymnasium, Monday lunchtime, something like that.

A few days later —

Who would have thought we would have had so many replies to that ad? I don't know how to *BEGIN* judging them.

We can rule out Mary Johnson for a start. She couldn't play a CD, let alone a drum solo. And *THIS* one expects us to provide her with a brand new drum kit!

This one's from a Pat Smith. I don't know any Pat Smith in our year. Do you?

I don't think so. Probably a new girl. Put her on the list.

On the day of the auditions —

She was *DREADFUL*.

She was the best so far, though. Maybe we could lick her into shape — *NOT!*

55

Where to rehearse became the next problem.

So, you see, Mrs Simpkins, we could make use of the music room at lunchtimes, without getting in anyone's way.

And it would be educational too, giving us some insight into the music business.

After a few anxious moments —

I don't see why not. Marie Anderson has already asked if she can have extra music time, to practise her singing for the contest. I wish you all luck!

As the day of the talent contest approached, the band decided to practise at Pat's house, as well as at the school —

You're sure your folks won't mind us practising here, Pat? We do make rather a lot of noise.

We make MUSIC, Liz. Not noise.

After the rehearsal —

You were great, Kerry. You've got a fantastic voice. We'll walk that contest, thanks to you.

'Course we will. But we need to practise, practise, practise. Especially if we have Marie to beat.

Next weekend, at Liz's house —

Kerry sounds great, and Pat's belting it out. All this hard work is paying off. We're getting better. But can we be good enough, soon enough?

The day of the contest arrived —

We're up next!

We need more practice! What made us think we were ready for this?

Get out there, and do your best. That's all anyone can expect.

Horse Laughs

61

playing the part

CONTINUED FROM PAGE 51.

Mrs Jones! Liam and I were rehearsing in the music room when his mates came in and caused trouble. Mr Hilditch gave us all a detention tomorrow — that means we'll miss a rehearsal!

I see, Kelly. I'll have a word with Mr Hilditch.

Later —

I've spoken to Mr Hilditch. You're off the hook, Kelly, but I'm afraid Liam isn't.

Oh, right — thanks.

I'll look forward to hearing Liam's new song tomorrow, AFTER his detention.

I'll tell him, Mrs Jones.

But I'll wait until he's on his own and not playing the fool in front of his mates.

After school —

Hey, Kel! Wait for me.

Oh, no! It's Joe. I'm not in the mood to chat to him.

You're spending an awful lot of time with Liam Brown.

Looks like he's sulking. I'm really getting fed up with Joe!

62

Next day, at rehearsal —

You'd better stand in for Liam until he arrives, Joe.

You mean gets out of detention, Mrs Jones, don't you?

Great leading man he is — in detention!

Yeah, okay. Let's get on with it, shall we?

Come on. You're supposed to know this. Just what have you been doing with super cool Brown?

Shut up, Joe!

That's enough, the two of you. We'll take a short break to calm things down.

When Liam arrived —

Let's hear this new song of yours, Liam.

And so —

Very impressive!

I think it's good, too.

I see. In that case you don't need me any more. Why not get Liam to rescore the whole thing. *I QUIT!*

Should I go after him?

Nah. Give him time to cool down first, Kelly. He'll be okay.

63

Sure enough —

I'm sorry, Kelly. Look, I've got two tickets for City's home game tonight. Wanna come?

You bet!

CONTINUED ON PAGE 71.

Eh? WHY?

You must have heard the stories about it being haunted, Jane! Danni Parker went up there last year and said that she saw a pair of glowing red eyes!

Yeah, but you can't believe everything SHE says!

It's said to be the ghost of a headmistress who taught here before the war — roaming the school at night! I think we should go and explore.

Ssh! Here come Tina and Susan.

What are you lot all being so secretive about?

Nothing that you'd be interested in, nosy! Clear off!

Just then, their teacher arrived —

I'm sure that stuck-up Saskia Poole and her friends were talking about the ghost of St Andrew's. I wonder what they're up to!

We'll find out later, Susan — don't worry.

At lunch —

MENU

Who fancies going up to the top floor for a look?

I don't think it's a good idea. If we're caught, we'll be in trouble.

We WON'T get caught! Where's your sense of adventure?

TRAY

Ssh . . . here come Susan and Tina again.

Let's go — we don't want them hearing where we're going!

So, after lunch —

Are you sure this is a good idea? It looks dark up there.

Don't be so scared, Jane. We're all here, so nothing will happen to you.

It does look a bit spooky. I don't want to go first.

Me, neither!

I'LL go first, cowards!

Soon, in the music room —

I think we should go back.

But we've only just got here! Let's go up this ladder into the attic.

So —

Wow! It's dark up here, but I can see a light switch.

Come down, Saskia! I think we should go.

67

But Saskia decided to explore —

You guys should really come up here and see this place — it's fantastic!

So, the others joined her —

These look like old school records. Maybe we can find out the name of the headmistress who's supposed to haunt this place? And more about her.

Look at this! It must be at least fifty years old. That could be the spooky headmistress!

She looks really strict, doesn't she?

Then —

Do you think this suits me?

Ha! Ha!

Suddenly —

What was that noise?

I don't know, but all of a sudden it's FREEZING in here!

I TOLD you this was a bad idea! Let's get out of here — NOW!

Look, maybe it was just the wind.

I don't care! I want to go!

Then —

There it is again! I'm sure it's NOT the wind!

Okay, we'll go — but ONLY because it's nearly the end of lunchtime. We'll come back again later.

But, when they'd gone —

What a laugh, Tina! We really gave them a scare!

I thought I was going to burst out laughing when they ran off like that. We'd better shut the window now — it's freezing!

What idiots! Imagine thinking there's REALLY a ghost!

Yeah! Now we've scared them away, that leaves the place to us.

Look at this old cloak — do you think it suits me, Tina?

Then —

T-T-Tina! There's something there — behind you!

Yeah — sure! Pull the other one!

70

playing the part

CONTINUED FROM PAGE 64.

You must be crazy, Kelly. Liam Brown spells trouble!

But he's really nice when he's on his own, Danni, honest! I've made up my mind — I'm dumping Joe for him.

Well, I still think you're daft.

You just don't know him like I do! He's considerate, caring and dead cute.

A couple of days later —

There are some places left on the theatre trip if anyone's interested.

I wonder if Liam would go. It would be great to go together.

But Joe's going! Still, after what happened after the footie match, he shouldn't be surprised if I dump him.

So —

That gang could have attacked me. I can do without a boyfriend like you, Joe. It's over.

Suits me. I'm sick of you going on and on about Liam. You'll soon find out what that yob is REALLY like!

When Kelly suggested the theatre trip —

I dunno, Kelly.

PLEASE, Liam — for me!

But Joe's going. He won't want me there.

He won't care — we've split up.

Yeah? In that case I'll ask my old lady for the ticket money.

Brilliant!

On the day of the trip —

Everyone's looking at Liam. They think he's a troublemaker, but he's different when his horrible mates aren't around.

Then, at the theatre —

He's engrossed in the play. This is the REAL Liam! I KNOW it.

In the interval —

I see what you mean about Liam, Kel. He's completely different on his own.

See, I told you.

On the way back —

I've had a super time. Liam's really great and I'm sure he likes me, too.

Next day, at Kelly's —

Me and Dad are only going out for a couple of hours. Try to get some of your homework done, Kelly.

Okay, Mum. 'Bye.

Then, a little later —

Hi, Kelly. Thought I'd come round to see how you're doing. We could have an extra rehearsal.

Yeah, good idea.

He MUST fancy me or he wouldn't come round.

72

Half an hour later —

Time for a break. Fancy a drink, Liam?

Yeah, thanks.

It's brilliant being alone with Liam — oh, no! There's the doorbell. Who can it be?

What are *YOU TWO* doing here?

Thought we'd check on how our mate was doing, eh, Liam?

That's okay, isn't it, Kelly? Can the lads have a drink, too?

Yeah, I guess.

Hey, mind that ornament. It's my mum's and it's very precious.

Don't worry, babe — I can juggle anything.

OOPS!

Not on form today, Mikey mate!

NOW look what you've done!

Time we were going, guys. See you, Kelly.

He's just going and leaving me to explain all this! Oh, *WHY* did his yobby mates have to come round and spoil things?

CONTINUED ON PAGE 78.

73

Pop-tastic Puzzlers!

Delve deep into your pop memory and see how well you can answer our quizzical questions!

Whose Album?

Okay, smarty pants! Who recorded each of these albums?

1. Aquarium.
2. Left Of The Middle.
3. Middle Of Nowhere.
4. My Way.
5. Life Thru A Lens.
6. Time.

A, B or C

1) Which member of 911 comes from Liverpool?
a) Spike.
b) Jimmy.
c) Lee.

2) "No Way, No Way" was a top 20 hit for which yummy band?
a) Strawberry.
b) Chocolate.
c) Vanilla.

3) Which pop legend returned to the limelight this year with the number 1 single, "Frozen"?
a) Madonna.
b) The Artist Formerly Known As Prince.
c) Michael Jackson.

4) Natalie Imbruglia appeared in which soap opera before becoming a huge star?
a) Home And Away.
b) Heartbreak High.
c) Neighbours.

5) Who sang about a "Brimful Of Asha"? Was it:
a) Cornershop?
b) Supermarket?
c) Chipshop?

6) Where were Nicole and Natalie Appleton from All Saints born?
a) America.
b) Canada.
c) Australia.

7) Victoria of the Spice Girls is engaged to footballer David Beckham. Which football team does he play for?
a) Manchester City.
b) Liverpool.
c) Manchester United.

8) Which ex-Take That star was not nominated for a Brit Award?
a) Gary Barlow.
b) Mark Owen.
c) Robbie Williams.

9) Abs from boy band, Five, has an equally famous girlfriend who appears in a top TV soap. Is she:
a) Gina Partrick in "Hollyoaks"?
b) Kelly Windsor in "Emmerdale"?
c) Toyah Battersby in "Coronation Street"?

10) Whose album was called "The Woman In Me"?
a) Robyn.
b) Celine Dion.
c) Louise.

GET LYRICAL!

**You know the song, but do you know the words?
Look at these lyrics and guess the song!**

1. And through it all she offers me protection,
   A lot of love and affection.
2. Down and dirty city, feeling out of place,
   Maybe she ran out of time.
3. A thousand words could never say enough,
   I know your history could turn us on.
4. Sometimes the feeling is right,
   You fall in love for the first time.
5. Where's the right in, all the fighting?
   Look at what you're doing.
6. Just another day,
   Sitting watching the clock.
7. There's nothing where he used to lie,
   Conversation has run dry.
8. Flexing vocabulary runs right through me,
   The alphabet runs right from A-Z.
9. What have I got to do,
   To get the message through to you?
10. Always been told I've got too much pride,
    Too independent to have you by my side.

GUESS WHO?

Can you guess the identity of the pop stars below?

1. I used to be a "Fresh Prince" and I used to hang out with a DJ called Jazzy Jeff. I starred in two blockbuster films, "Independence Day" and "Men In Black", and I spent 1998 "Getting Jiggy Wit' It". Who am I?

2. I may be small but I'm a big star! My brother is a pop singer, too, but he sings with four other guys. This year I had a "Crush On You", but then I found a "Crazy Little Party Girl". Who am I?

3. I am the biggest selling female artist in the world. I was born in Quebec, Canada, and I released my first single when I was only 12 years old! I also like to sing songs in my native language, French, and last year I had a huge hit with "My Heart Will Go On", from the film, "Titanic". Who am I?

4. I was born in Lewisham, London, on 4th November, 1974. I went to the Italia Conti Stage School where I made friends with a girl called Kelle. After I left school, I joined an all girl band (with Kelle) which became very successful. I left to pursue a solo career and my bloke is a footballer. Who am I?

ANSWERS

GET LYRICAL!
1. "Angels" — Robbie Williams.
2. "Never Give Up On The Good Times" — Spice Girls.
3. "Story Of Love" — OTT.
4. "Doctor Jones" — Aqua.
5. "Where's The Love" — Hanson.
6. "Party People . . . Friday Night" — 911.
7. "Torn" — Natalie Imbruglia.
8. "Never Ever" — All Saints.
9. "I'm A Man Not A Boy" — North And South.
10. "Show Me Love" — Robyn.

GUESS WHO?
1. Will Smith.
2. Aaron Carter.
3. Celine Dion.
4. Louise.

A, B OR C?

WHOSE ALBUM?	
1. B.	6. B.
2. C.	7. C.
3. A.	8. B.
4. C.	9. A.
5. A.	10. C.

1. Aqua.
2. Natalie Imbruglia.
3. Hanson.
4. Usher.
5. Robbie Williams.
6. Peter Andre.

IN THE MIX!

Unravel the anagrams below and find four top pop hits!

1) I HATE VEGI OVALL — BACKSTREET BOYS
2) CHAIN BY A LOUD YOB — BOYZONE
3) TOUGH NEW SHOT HIT LEG — FIVE
4) ALL CART GRITTY RELY ZIP — AARON CARTER

Now try your luck with these brilliant boys and great girls pop puzzles!

Pop-tastic puzzlers! BOYS & GIRLS

BACKSTREET OR BOYZONE?

Here's a top test for you! Can you guess what the next line to each song is, what it's called and whether it's a Boyzone or Backstreet Boys song?

1) Even in my heart I see.
2) I let you in and you let me down.
3) People say I'm crazy and that I am blind.
4) This world has lost its glory.

Swap Shop!

These top girlies got their shopping bags muddled up. Can you sort out who owns what?

NATALIE IMBRUGLIA	MANCHESTER UNITED SCARF
CLEOPATRA	RED HAIR DYE
VICTORIA (POSH SPICE)	KOALA BEAR TEDDY
LENE (AQUA)	3T ALBUM

IN THE MIX!

Unravel the anagrams below to reveal 4 top pop girl power hits!

1) I PILE CUPS FORE YU — SPICE GIRLS.
2) TED DUE HERB RING — ALL SAINTS.
3) DO MED NIGHTEY MOUSE BOY — SHOLA AMA.
4) SO U GET A LONG DRAIN — LOUISE.

Star search

See if you can find the names of the 26 pop acts listed in the grid below!

- ★ ALL SAINTS
- ★ CLEOPATRA
- ★ DANNII
- ★ ETERNAL
- ★ GINA G
- ★ KYLIE
- ★ LOUISE
- ★ MADONNA
- ★ MARIAH CAREY
- ★ NATALIE IMBRUGLIA
- ★ SHOLA AMA
- ★ SPICE GIRLS
- ★ VANILLA
- ★ AARON CARTER
- ★ ANT AND DEC
- ★ BACKSTREET BOYS
- ★ BOYZONE
- ★ GARY BARLOW
- ★ HANSON
- ★ KAVANA
- ★ NO AUTHORITY
- ★ NORTH AND SOUTH
- ★ OTT
- ★ PETER ANDRE
- ★ ROBBIE WILLIAMS
- ★ WILL MELLOR

```
N O A U T H O R I T Y M A M A A L O H S
B O K G A R Y B A R L O W N C W F A P Y
C P R O F C L I V D Z M F D A N N I I O
A V E T E R N A L E U A G K Z S C L O B
N M D P H K E X U U J W D F O E H G U T
N X G O L A H Z E I M O G N G C Z U J E
O L I U N W N S W B T K C I T S L R H E
D A N I E T I D O B V C R F Y R N B U R
A T A R N U K F S N F L K P C E I M V T
M J G O O O K J V O S N U W R V D I R S
A N C L Z U D G T B U Y E D N S I E R K
S X J L Y I N T W Z P T N H K J Q I I C
T C L E O P A T R A R A H P S W H L X A
N E X M B D V R E T R A C N O R A A L B
I O G L U A P I C E L I F Z L M D T S E
A F O L N E X O T G G Q Z R M H D A H W
S H F I B I V E P G C E D D N A T N A P
L J L W Q L P Y N P I D Q X R W Q U M R
L L Y J V V Y E R A C H A I R A M C Z K G
A N A V A K S M A I L L I W E I B B O R
```

SAINT OR SPICE

Do you know the next line to each of these hits? Have a go and while you're at it, guess which song it's from and whether it's by All Saints or the Spice Girls!

1) When you're feeling sad and low.
2) If you wanna have a good time.
3) I don't ever wanna feel like I did that day.
4) The race is on to get out of the bottom.

Swap Shop!

All these pop stars went shopping and somehow managed to get their bags mixed up! Can you match each boy to his buy?

JAMES (North and South)	HERCULES VIDEO
AARON CARTER	GREEN HAIR DYE
STEPHEN (Boyzone)	LIVERPOOL FOOTBALL KIT
JIMMY (911)	NINJA TURTLE TOY

playing the part

CONTINUED FROM PAGE 73.

There's something I want to ask you, Kel . . .

He's going to ask me for a date!

But, just then —

So, HERE you are!

DAD! What are you doing here?

Looking for YOU! I might have known you'd be up to no good with the likes of HIM!

We're only having a Coke, Dad. I was about to ring . . .

Tara phoned for you and told us the rehearsal had finished early. I've been worried sick, looking for you.

TARA! Huh! She's trying to land me in it so she can get Liam!

I'm sorry, Dad. I thought it would be okay to go to the café, as we finished early. I'll tell you next time.

There won't BE a next time! You're grounded for the rest of the month!

Grounded! But what about the show?

It's your own fault, Kelly.

But they can't stop me being in the show — THEY CAN'T!

CONTINUED ON PAGE 97.

Disco Babes!

Rhona and Caroline are cousins and they both live on farms.

"We've got lots of messy jobs to do, like mucking out the ponies," Rhona told us. "We nearly always wear jeans and boots, so we want a cool look for Christmas."

How could we refuse? We whisked the girls off to the photographer's where Karen, the make-up artist, was at their beck and call.

RHONA

SKIN: Not much make-up was needed here as Rhona has lovely clear skin. Karen used a tinted moisturiser in a natural shade to even out skin tones. A light dusting of powder set the make-up and got rid of any shiny bits.

EYES: Karen brushed a pale shimmery pink all over Rhona's eyelids, right up to her brows. Then she chose a violety purple and brushed this on at the outer corners of Rhona's eyes. A tiny bit of soft, shimmery grey eyeliner was smudged under the lower lashes. Browny black mascara finished things off.

CHEEKS: A soft, peachy-pink blusher was brushed on to the fattest part of Rhona's cheeks.

LIPS: Lipstick to match the blusher was used and finished with a coat of clear lip-gloss for extra sparkle.

HAIR: Rhona's hair was lovely and shiny, so Karen made it look extra-smooth by flattening it with some hot straighteners. Two mini-clips in a shimmery purple finished the look.

CAROLINE

Caroline had lovely, soft hair, so before starting the make-up Karen put some large velcro rollers in it. This would give it more body and bounce. Caroline wouldn't let us take a photo of her wearing her curlers!

SKIN: Like Rhona, Caroline only needed some tinted moisturiser and a dusting of powder.

EYES: Karen used a white/gold eyeshadow all over Caroline's eyes right up to her brows. Then she brushed a soft lime green over the eyelids and blended the two colours together. A slightly darker green at the outer corners was also added. Caroline has very dark lashes, so only a tiny amount of mascara was needed to complete the look.

CHEEKS: A peachy brown blusher was brushed on with a chunky brush.

LIPS: Like Rhona, Caroline's lipstick matched her blusher and was finished with clear lipgloss.

HAIR: Karen took out the velcro rollers and gently brushed through Caroline's hair. Then, using a hot brush, she smoothed it out and curled the ends up. Hairclips to match Caroline's top added the finishing touch.

> **CLOTHES:** Velvet tops from *Bhs.* Purple mini-clips from *C&A.* Green hairclips from *New Look.*

Ready To Go!

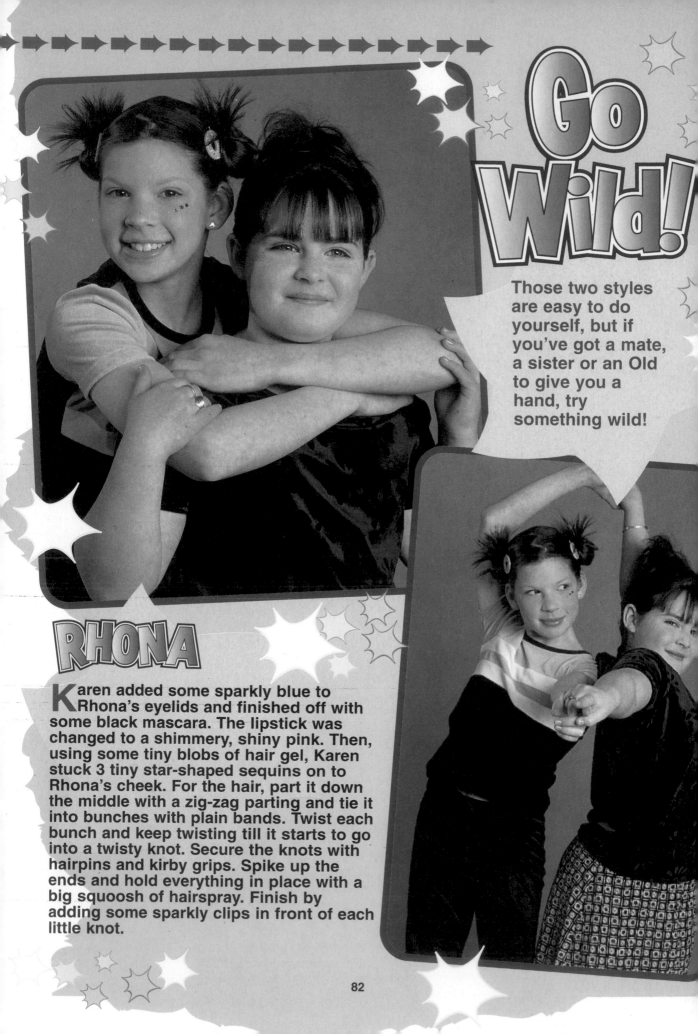

Go Wild!

Those two styles are easy to do yourself, but if you've got a mate, a sister or an Old to give you a hand, try something wild!

RHONA

Karen added some sparkly blue to Rhona's eyelids and finished off with some black mascara. The lipstick was changed to a shimmery, shiny pink. Then, using some tiny blobs of hair gel, Karen stuck 3 tiny star-shaped sequins on to Rhona's cheek. For the hair, part it down the middle with a zig-zag parting and tie it into bunches with plain bands. Twist each bunch and keep twisting till it starts to go into a twisty knot. Secure the knots with hairpins and kirby grips. Spike up the ends and hold everything in place with a big squoosh of hairspray. Finish by adding some sparkly clips in front of each little knot.

CAROLINE

Karen changed the green eyeshadow to a purply blue and used blue/black mascara for a night-time look. Deep pink lipstick with clear gloss finished the basic make-up. For extra sparkle, Karen then added some silver glitter gel just beneath Caroline's eyes. For this hairstyle, pull your hair back into a low pony tail, but don't tie with a band. Lift the end of the pony tail above your head and start to twist. The hair should roll in toward the back of your head. Secure the roll with lots of grips and pins. Fluff up the ends into a messy look and give everything a good blast of hairspray. Put a sparkly clip in at the front for extra colour.

Get dancing!

CLOTHES: Purple and navy velvet top, *Marks & Spencer.*
Silky navy trousers and lilac hairclips, *C&A.*
Silver trainers, *Tammy.*
Navy velvet top, *Bhs.*
Wrap-over skirt, *Marks & Spencer.*
Silver hairclip, *C&A*

KAREN'S TIPS

♣Too much make-up looks terrible, so don't be tempted to slap everything on. It's easy to add a little more colour a bit at a time, but it's hard to get rid of too much.

♣Don't forget your powder. It will keep your make-up in place and stop you from looking shiny. If you don't have any, a LITTLE talc will do the same job. Add too much and you'll look like a ghost!

♣You can use Vaseline for a lipgloss. A small tub doesn't cost much, lasts for AGES and will keep your lips nice and soft, too. Get it from chemists and supermarkets.

♣Dabbing on a little tea tree oil will help zap any spots that pop up. You can get it from the Body Shop, Superdrug and health food stores.

♣If you have really pale eyebrows (Rhona's are quite fair), brush a small amount of brown eyeshadow through them. This will give your eyes more shape.

♣Strips cut from an old pair of (clean!) tights make great hair-friendly hairbands. Choose a colour that's nearest your hair colour.

JOIN US BEHIND THE SCENES AT BYKER GROVE AND MEET THE

NEW KIDS ON THE BLOCK

Wait a minute, though. What's that wailing noise? It couldn't be, *could it?*

Then Stephen tries some clothes on Nick and Gary. Gary's jacket is going to need altering, but Nick's dead chuffed with his red shirt!

Here's Siobhan, Jade, Louise, Gary and Nick five of the newest cast members — waiting show you how things work behind the scenes the Byker Grove studios. Looking like a small castle, all the action inside and outside the youth club is filmed here at The Mitre. Rumour has it that it even has its own ghost! As if!

First stop the Wardrobe Department. Costume designers decide on the style for each character. Unfortunately, they *all* can't be trendy — some *have* to be naff! Caroline selects outfits for the girls and luckily they all look happy with them.

Jade, Siobhan and Louise iscover the jewellery store. 's a treasure chest of every type of accessory you can think of . . .

. . . including sunglasses! The guys think they look dead cool in their shades! Men in Blue and Black!

MORE ON NEXT PAGE

NEW KIDS ON THE BLOCK
Continued

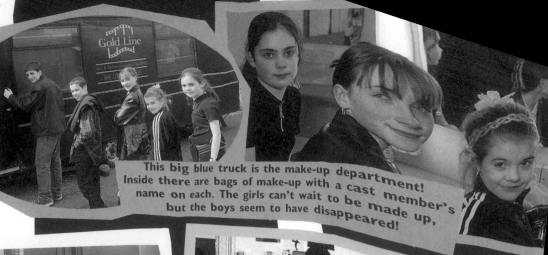

This big blue truck is the make-up department! Inside there are bags of make-up with a cast member's name on each. The girls can't wait to be made up, but the boys seem to have disappeared!

Lunchtime! There's always a great choice of scrummy meals at the canteen. The hardest part is choosing!

After lunch, everyone gathers round Dee, the production secretary, who informs the cast where they have to be and when. Dee has been with Byker Grove from the very beginning and knows everything about everybody — unfortunately, she isn't telling!

Then the gang goes to see the director, Tony Kish. He's planning out the next episodes and tells the cast where they will be filming, which could be anywhere from the seaside to a shopping mall.

Jade, Louise and Siobhan have a go on the climbing frame. Ten years of 'Grovers' have trodden these ropes!

Almost time to go, but not before our famous five meet up at the famous snack counter in the games room. And they're still smiling even though they've just heard that all the drinks and chocolate snacks are strictly for filming use only!

It's A Date!

JULY

S	–	4	11	18	25
M	–	5	12	19	26
Tu	–	6	13	20	27
W	–	7	14	21	28
Th	1	8	15	22	29
F	2	9	16	23	30
S	3	10	17	24	31

PAMELA ANDERSON

KAVANA

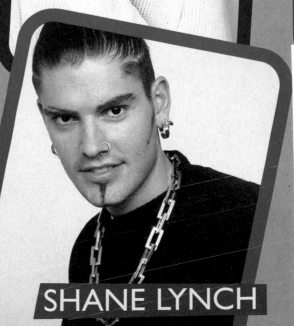

SHANE LYNCH

WRITE ON!

Michael Jackson
MG News
International
P.O. Box 7998
Bournemouth
BH1 4XL

Janet Jackson
c/o Virgin Records
553-597 Harrow
Road
London
W10 4RH

Kavana
P.O. Box 21
London
W10 6BR

Eternal
P.O. Box 460
High Wycombe
Bucks
HP12 4BR

IMPORTANT DATES!

Liv Tyler — *1st*
Pamela Anderson — *1st*
Shane Lynch
(Boyzone) — *3rd*
Tom Hanks — *9th*
Anna Friel — *12th*
St Swithin's Day — *15th*
TJ Jackson (3T) — *16th*
Robin Williams — *21st*
Matt Le Blanc
(Friends) — *25th*
Lisa Kudrow
(Friends) — *30th*

It's A Date!

AUGUST

S	1	8	15	22	29
M	2	9	16	23	30
Tu	3	10	17	24	31
W	4	11	18	25	–
Th	5	12	19	26	–
F	6	13	20	27	–
S	7	14	21	28	–

GERI HALLIWELL

MIKEY GRAHAM

MADONNA

WRITE ON!

Kylie Minogue
75 Green Lane
Shepperton
Middlesex
TW17 8DU

Madonna
c/o Warner
Brothers
28 Kensington
Church Street
London
W8 4EP

Steve McManaman
c/o Liverpool F.C.
Anfield Road
Liverpool
L4 0TH

Tom Cruise
c/o PMK
955 Carillo Drive
200 Los Angeles
CA 90048
USA

IMPORTANT DATES!

Gina G — *3rd*
Spike Dawbarn (911) — *5th*
Geri Halliwell (Spice Girls) — *6th*
Whitney Houston — *9th*
Mikey Graham (Boyzone) — *15th*
Madonna — *16th*
Matthew Perry (Friends) — *19th*
Howie Dorough
(Backstreet Boys) — *22nd*

IMPORTANT DATES!

Niall O'Neill (OTT) — 11th
Adam Mates (OTT) — 18th
Liam Gallagher (Oasis) — 21st
Jimmy Constable (911) — 21st
Declan Donnelly
(Ant & Dec) — 25th
Will Smith — 25th
Gwyneth Paltrow — 27th

WRITE ON!

Ewan McGregor
c/o 27 Floral Street
London
WC2 9DF

Hanson
Hitz List
P.O. Box 703136
Tulsa
Oklahoma
74170 USA

Will Mellor
Fan Club
P.O. Box 14889
London
W7 1WN

Pulp
c/o Pulp People
P.O. Box 87
Sheffield
S6 2YZ

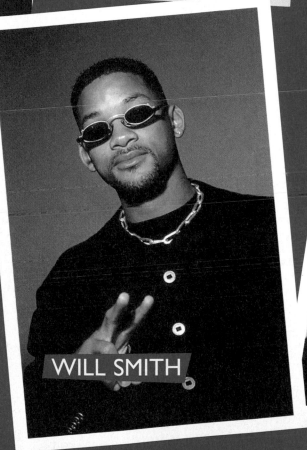

WILL SMITH

EWAN McGREGOR

SEPTEMBER

OTT

S	—	5	12	19	26
M	—	6	13	20	27
Tu	—	7	14	21	28
W	1	8	15	22	29
Th	2	9	16	23	30
F	3	10	17	24	—
S	4	11	18	25	—

Anna changes into her show outfit and swots up on her lines.

PLEASED AS PUNCH!

Ever wondered how a Punch and Judy show is put together? We take a peek behind the scenes as reader, Anna Lassiter, shows us how it's done!

90

Aaw, what a lovely family! It's Mr Punch and his wife, Judy, with their baby.

Meet the rest of the cast! These puppets are Merlin the magician and Joey the clown, who is named after the famous 11th century clown, Joey Grimaldi.

Mr Punch shows us his slap stick — two pieces of wood which make a slapping noise when he hits anything. Ouch, I bet it hurts!

The puppets are kept hanging up in the booth so the puppeteer can reach them easily.

Time for the show and Anna gets down to some serious entertaining!

Everybody has heard of Punch and Judy shows but do you know anything about the history of them? The puppets originally came from Italy but somehow managed to end up in Britain, where they were adopted as the country's national puppets. They can be traced back as early as 1660! Also, did you know that Mr Punch is always operated on the puppeteer's right hand? They originally toured the country, acting as a news service (there were no papers, radio or TV!) and were merchandised in the form of door stops, china teapots, mugs and even walking stick handles!

n the other side e booth Mr Punch d Judy are waving to the crowds.

The show is over and Anna takes a bow. "It was hard work, but lots of fun!" she says.

SHARON LOUISE

Sharon's not too keen on Louise's choice of outfit.

Twice as Nice or Double

Is being a twin twice as nice or double trouble? We decided to ask Sharon and Louise what it's really like to be half of a twin twosome.

"THERE are advantages and disadvantages," the girls told us. "It can be annoying when teachers get us confused but, on the other hand, we can confuse people for a laugh. We also get our clothes mixed up a lot, but we can share when we want to — even although Sharon is a bit bigger." It also helps that the girls have different favourite colours. Sharon likes red, while Louise is well into pink.

"We try not to dress alike all the time and we have had our hair cut differently in the past. At the moment it's the same (although Louise likes to tie it back) but we might change the styles again." And what about gifts? Do the girls like to get different things?

"Since we were small we've had the same presents. Once Dad bought us dolls which were different — one had dark hair and one was blonde — and we both wanted the blonde one. So now we always get exactly the same to save arguments."

One big plus is that the girls can share secrets — although they don't tell each other who they fancy — and they also share hobbies like dancing and swimming. "We're never lonely," they said, "although it can be difficult to get time on our own. And if

92

Time for a nosh-up. Sharon loves pasta, but Louise sticks to pizza.

Cool shades, girls, but we can still tell who's who.

Trouble?

Sharon goes for Eternal while Louise picks Hanson. Both like Spice Girls and Boyzone.

...e fall out we can't ...et away from each ...ther. That's a ...efinite ...isadvantage!"

But, overall, the ...irls like being ...wins. "If one of us ...ill, we look after ...ach other and, ...lthough we're in ...ifferent classes at ...chool and have ...ther good ...iends, we ...ways meet up at lunch and home ...me. Really, we're never far away ...om each other."

They're also huge Leonardo Di Caprio fans. Guess their favourite film!

Best friends as well as sisters.

Make 'n'

It's easy to give lots of old things
look in next to no time. Brighten u
bits 'n' pieces to really cheer up you

MIRROR, MIRROR

Your mirror can always look cheery — even if you don't!

You will need:
old mirror
paint
coloured felt squares (from fabric shops)
glue
sequins or beads

What to do:
1. If your mirror has wooden bits on it like ours, paint them with a bright colour (we used poster paints).
2. Choose a design for your frame and cut it to fit from felt (it won't fray). We did a wave design with one colour on the short sides and another colour on the long sides. If you make a pattern from paper first, it's easy to do the corner joins (see diagram).
3. Glue the felt frame onto the mirror. If you like, you can glue sequins or little beads onto the felt to make it extra sparkly.

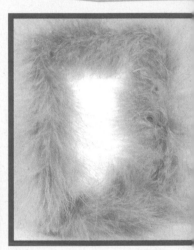

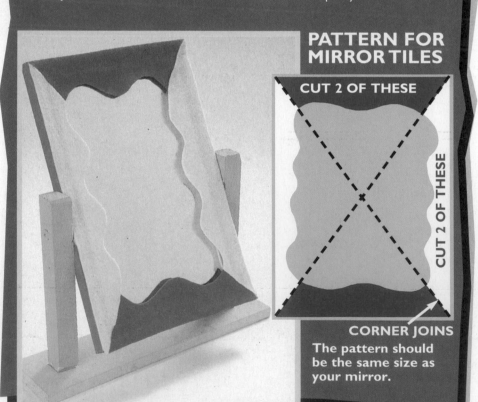

PATTERN FOR MIRROR TILES

CUT 2 OF THESE

CUT 2 OF THESE

CORNER JOINS

The pattern should be the same size as your mirror.

PICTURE PERFECT

Updating an old picture frame into something fluffy and funky is really simple.

You will need:
old photo frame
glue
marabou trim (measure each edge of your frame and add them all together to find out how much you need)
glue
coloured card or paper (we used silver wrapping paper)

What to do:
1. Glue the fluffy trim round the edg of the frame.
2. Cut a piece of coloured card or paper to fit inside the frame. This makes a groovy backing for your photo.
3. Add your chosen picture and tha it.

Do

ew
ome
oom.

HANGIN' OUT

hese little hooks are dead
andy for hanging up odds 'n'
nds. We made them from an
ld mug rack.

You will need:
ld mug rack or coat hook
ack
andpaper
aint
lue
m of marabou trim
from fabric shops)

What to do:

1. If the mug rack has a shiny,
varnished finish, rub it with the
sandpaper to roughen the surface.
This makes it easy for the paint to
stick to the wood.

2. Start to paint. We used poster
paints, but emulsion match pots are
also good. You may need two coats.

3. When it's dry, cut the fluffy
marabou trim into little pieces and
glue a piece on to the end of each
peg.

Wildlife
HARP SEAL

playing the part

CONTINUED FROM PAGE 80.

But you *CAN'T* ground me! I'll miss the show!

Well, you should have thought of that before you went off with that troublemaker, Liam Brown.

This is *SO* unfair! And it's all that Tara Lord's fault for landing me in it!

Next day, at school —

I hope I didn't get you into any *TROUBLE* yesterday, Kelly!

What do *YOU* think, Tara?

She's after Liam. *THAT'S* why she wants me out of the way!

At lunchtime, Kelly told Mrs Jones, the Drama teacher —

. . . so I'll have to drop out of the show, miss.

We can't have that. I'll have a word with your parents, Kelly.

So, after school —

. . . and I'll make sure that Kelly goes straight home after each rehearsal.

Very well, Kelly can still take part if she follows these conditions.

Huh! They make me feel like a little kid!

At the next rehearsal —

I'm really annoyed with Mum and Dad. They just don't understand, Joe!

Look, Kel, don't come whingeing to me. That's what happens when you hang out with yobs.

At the dress rehearsal —

Come on, Kelly, that's your cue. You won't be able to miss cues tomorrow night!

S-sorry, Mrs Jones.

I keep thinking about Liam. Why must everyone think the worst of him?

It's no good. I can't concentrate — I can't go through with it!

Hey, what's up? Your mistake wasn't *THAT* bad.

I-I guess I'm just letting things get on top of me, Liam.

Come on, it's just a bit of nerves. You know you'll be fine.

Do-do you think so?

Yeah, trust me.

He *MUST* really like me or he wouldn't care so much.

The show was on for two nights. On the first night —

Break a leg, Liam!

Yeah, yeah! Just give *ME* a break, okay. And don't make any trouble!

I hope Liam's yobby mates do behave themselves. *THEY'RE* the troublemakers — not him!

But, when Liam walked on stage —

GO, LIAM, GO!

Oh, no! They've started already!

98

But, at the end —

MORE! MORE!

This is brilliant! I was wrong about Liam's mates. They kept quiet during the show and now they're cheering the loudest!

I hope the show goes as well tomorrow night when Mum and Dad are here.

And, the following night —

Liam is even better tonight. Mum and Dad are sure to be impressed.

At the interval —

How about a cast party tomorrow at my place? My olds are going out.

You're on, Tara!

Huh! Bet my mum and dad won't let ME go!

After the show —

It was excellent, Kelly. We're both very proud of you.

And the lad was good, too.

WOW! Dad's actually saying something good about Liam!

There's a cast party tomorrow round at Tara's. Is it okay if I go?

I don't see why not. You've worked hard, so you deserve a bit of fun.

And Liam won't have his mates around him. This is my chance to get off with him before Tara does!

CONTINUED ON PAGE 110.

Tinker's Tale

THE ponies were at the moor gate again. Astrid got off the school bus as it stopped at the green and went to see them. One of them, a bay yearling, was always a little bolder than the rest. Astrid took out the apple which she had saved from lunch. The other ponies backed away as she approached the gate, turning towards the open sweep of hills, heather and gorse that made up the wild landscape of Exmoor, but the young pony hesitated, ears pricked towards Astrid.

"Hello," she said softly. "It's me again . . . and I've brought you something nice."

She set the apple down near the colt, whose ears stayed pricked.

"There," she said. "It's quite safe . . . I won't try to catch you."

She stood still while the colt reached out his neck, feeling for the apple with his soft lips, his eyes still on Astrid. Then he had it. As he crunched, Astrid held out her hand, and just for a moment the colt stretched towards her, and she felt his whiskers and his warm breath touch her hand. Then the stallion with the herd whinnied and all the ponies set off at a canter across the boggy ground, with the bay colt galloping after them. Astrid sighed, and turned for home.

"Hello love, you're late, aren't you?" asked her mum, as she walked into the cottage.

"I was talking to one of the ponies," Astrid told her. "I do wish I could buy it. The moorland foals don't cost much at the sales and I have been saving up for a long time."

"But they still cost more than we can afford and, besides, they're too wild," her mother pointed out. "You have a riding lesson twice a month. I'm afraid it's all we can manage for now."

Astrid had expected her mother to say these words. But she was still disappointed.

PONY SALE

It was autumn, time for the pony sale. Astrid watched the men starting to drive the ponies down from the moor. The bay yearling would probably be among them, unless he managed to avoid the drive, as some youngsters always did. All the ponies had owners, farmers with common grazing rights on the moor, but they were unhandled, and wild as hares.

"But I could tame one, if only I had a real chance," thought Astrid longingly. There seemed little chance of that, though, and Astrid sighed as she watched the ponies starting to stream down the hill, driven on by the men on ponies with their dogs running alongside.

When she got home that evening, Astrid hurried out onto the moor. There was just the chance her bay yearling had been missed — she really hoped so! The moor near the gate was deserted, and Astrid ran up the steep path which led to a view of the next sweeping valley. It was worth the climb because, from the top, she could see two ponies among the gorse, a dun and a bay.

"Tinker!" Astrid called out the name she had secretly given him. "Oh, Tinker, you're still there. You're safe."

She hurried down the hill, but although the pony had been growing tamer over the last few months, the drive had scared him, and he and his companion took one look at her and cantered off. Astrid was disappointed. Now she would have to start trying to tame him all over again. Was it worth it, when there was so little chance of him ever being her own?

RESCUE IN THE SNOW

Autumn turned to winter, and the bitter winds swept across the moor. Tinker and his friend were often near the gate, sheltering, and Astrid took tit-bits to them, but the colt remained shy. Then a week of bright, cold weather gave way to snow, and by morning the streams were frozen and the moor white. After breakfast Astrid went out to look for Tinker. Surely he wouldn't be far from shelter today?

At the high view-point she stopped to gaze round at the white moor ... snowy slopes and rocks which the wind had

blown clear. At last she saw him, a spot of colour among all the white. But he wasn't moving. He stood, head down, tail tucked in, close to a half-buried sheep fence. Astrid began to run, suddenly sure that something was wrong.

Tinker's front leg was stretched in front of him, and Astrid dug carefully until she found the trouble. His leg was entangled in a square of the wire stock fencing, trapping him, and the bitter night had taken all his warmth and will to struggle. There was dried blood on the snow, and as Astrid tugged away the wire she saw the deep cut on his leg. At last he was free, but he stood still, shivering, and dazed by cold. Now Astrid could touch him, stroke his neck, and rub his ears until a faint warmth came into them. She took off her scarf, and put it round his neck, and very slowly, encouraging him all the way, she persuaded him to follow her up the hill, and down the track to the gate. There, her mother was anxiously waiting.

"He's hurt, and half-frozen," Astrid explained. "He can go in the shed, can't he? I can get hay and straw from the farm."

"I suppose so, but you must tell the farmer who owns the

ponies," said her mother. "And that's a nasty cut."

The farmer who owned the colt was grateful to Astrid for saving Tinker. So grateful that, seeing how much the colt meant to her, he offered to sell Astrid the pony at a bargain price.

"The sale's over for the year and it will save me the cost of food," he said.

"Oh, Mum, please let me ... I've got enough money saved," Astrid begged, and her mother nodded.

"All right," she said. "I'm sure Dad will agree. But we must have an agreement in writing with you, Mr Lindberg," she added, to the farmer.

It took the rest of the winter to get Tinker well, and much hard work and anguish from Astrid as she fed and cleaned and cared for him, but by spring he was sound, fat and lively again. Turned out in a neighbour's paddock, Astrid watched him gallop round, and come to her call. It had been a hard fight, but worth it, and she looked forward to riding him on the moor, once he had been properly tamed and broken. Tinker was hers at last.

THE END

sweet sisters

It looks like the sisters from the picture!

But it CAN'T be! I mean, it was painted in 1856!

That's right, but we are the GHOSTS of the sisters.

AAAHH!

Come, now! There is no need to be scared!

Well, not for YOU, but if we find the rogue who has stolen our portrait, it will be a different matter.

That is why we are here — to investigate the theft. Otherwise, we'd be haunting much nicer places!

I fancy Disneyland.

Don't be silly! We cannot haunt Disneyland, Clara — we never lived anywhere near Disneyland!

There is no point in trying to reason with her, Bea! She ALWAYS knows best!

Sweet Sisters, the picture was called, but they don't seem very sweet to me!

WE'D like to get the painting back, too.

Then we shall work together!

I just can't imagine anyone stealing it. It wasn't valuable, and . . .

Who told you THAT? Of COURSE it's valuable!

Soon it was time for afternoon lessons —

Must you go? We'll wait for you here again tomorrow.

They weren't happy when you said the painting wasn't worth much!

Yeah, they're not very sweet sisters, are they? This is all SO weird!

Next day, at lunchtime —

There they are again — it wasn't a dream!

You know, at first I thought they were being big-headed saying the painting was valuable because it was of them, but maybe there's more to it . . .

So —

I was wondering who painted the picture?

Our dear Uncle Teddy. All his other paintings have his full signature — Oliver T. Smythe. But this one he signed 'Teddy' — our pet name for him.

You must have heard of him — he was VERY famous.

Umm — I don't really know Victorian art.

He was extremely famous.

So, later that afternoon —

Oliver T. Smythe? His paintings sell for thousands! Yes, I suppose 'Sweet Sisters' was in his style.

So, if we got the painting back, and got permission to sell it, the school would have enough money for the repairs it needs?

I have already stated that! Must you repeat EVERYTHING?

We'll — er — check with our Art teacher.

Yes, I suppose so. Now, girls, I'd like you to sign this card — it's a going-away card for the caretaker. He's having to leave.

Oh, that's a pity.

Later —

We *MUST* find that painting! I reckon it's been taken by someone who knew its true value.

How about a descendant of the sisters' Uncle Teddy? Let's go and ask them about their relatives — and if they'll allow us to sell the painting if we find it.

And, so —

Yes, of course you can sell it. Now, let me see . . . there were the Smythes — which included us and Uncle Teddy — and the Hadley-Smythes, who were dreadful people. We all fell out over a hundred years ago.

REALLY? Our *CARETAKER* is called Hadley! What if he's a descendant of *THEIR* relatives who knows the value of the painting? He's leaving, too!

So —

There he is — getting into his car!

Yes, he is a Hadley-Smythe, all right. You can tell by his ears.

Right, he's gone. If only we could get inside his house to see if he has the painting hidden somwhere.

That's hardly a serious problem!

And —

It's okay for *YOU*, but *WE* can't walk through walls!

No . . .

106

. . . but WE can now unlock the door for you!

And, after a search —

Here it is!

Er, I don't like to spoil things . . .

. . . but Mr Hadley is coming back!

I'll call the police!

WE will disappear . . .

Huh! They've just vanished and left us to it!

The police won't be long. Let's hide!

But, just then —

Hey, what's going on in here?

Then —

HELP!

107

And —

Ha! Ha! I don't think the sisters HAVE left us to it!

THE END

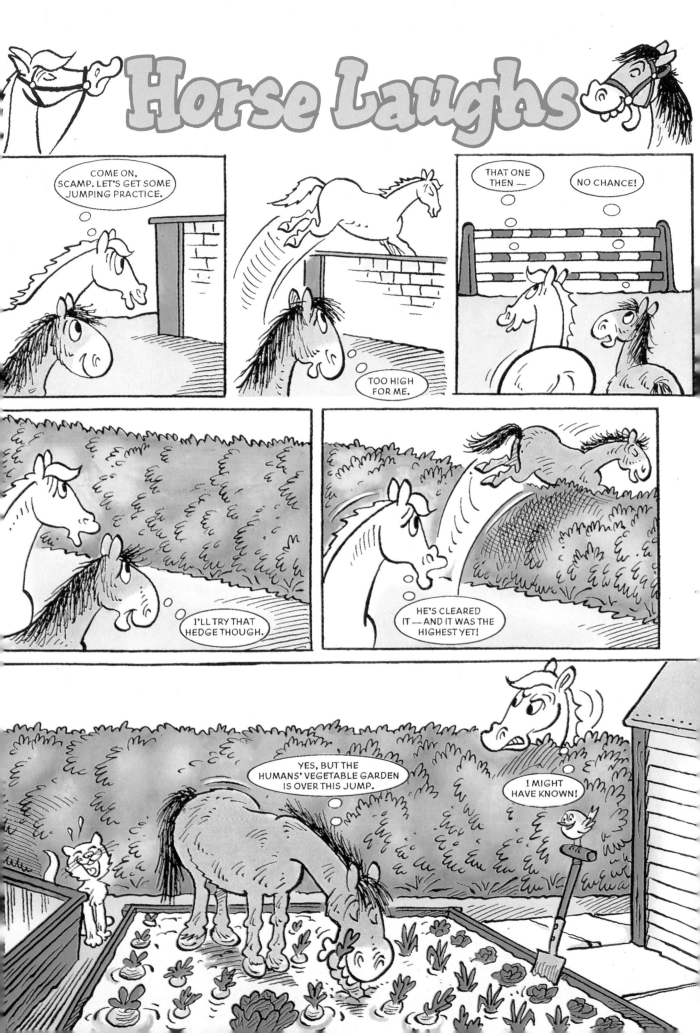

playing the part

At Tara's party —

CONTINUED FROM PAGE 99.

Just look at Tara, trying to chat up Liam! Well *I'M* going to put a stop to *THAT!*

Oh, hi, Kelly. I was hoping you'd be allowed to come.

No probs! Mum and Dad were so pleased with the show that I'm no longer grounded. They thought you were good, too!

WOW! He's asked me for a date. But I don't think Mum and Dad are ready for that — I'll keep it secret.

Cool! They won't mind if I take you to the pictures tomorrow then, eh?

So, next evening —

I'm just off round Danni's, Mum.

Okay, love. Don't be late.

At the cinema —

Come on, Kel. The movie's about to start!

110

Fancy a sweet?

Thanks, Liam.

Liam's so nice. If only more people could see this side of him.

But, soon —

MUST you keep rustling those sweets? I'm trying to listen to the film!

Keep your hair on, mate! Here, have one on us!

BULLSEYE!

LIAM! That wasn't very nice.

Then, when they left —

Oh, NO! There's one of our neighbours. I'd better not let her see me or she'll tell Mum!

Later, back home —

I know I should tell Mum and Dad about going out with Liam, but they wouldn't approve. And no way am I giving up Liam!

So, on Kelly's next date —

I'm just off to the youth club disco. Danni's dad is bringing us home.

Have a nice, time, Kelly!

Soon —

Hi, Liam. Sorry I'm a bit late.

No sweat, babe. I've just arrived, too.

Inside —

Ah, Coke! Just what I want!

HEY! That's MINE!

111

THE END

112

SUMMER FUN!

Stephanie and Leanne are friends and are in the same class at school. We decided to give them a fun look for summer. Flowers were the theme and soon they were blossoming everywhere.

Step by Step

BASE

EYES

CHEEKS

1. Give yourself a good base to start. Even out your skin tone with a natural tinted moisturiser — summer skins don't need any more. Dust lightly with powder to make your base last longer.

2. Next, do your eyes. Brush a pale, shimmery shade all over the eye area up to the brows. Choose a nice summer colour and blend it in at the outer corners of the eyes. We picked a coral pink for Leanne and a lilac for Stephanie. Finish with one coat of mascara.

3. Use a light pearly peach or pink on your cheeks.

4. Finish with a soft lipstick. We used a coral shade on Leanne to match her eyeshadow.

5. Now for the fun bit. Paint some little flowers on your cheeks. We used face paints, but you can use eyeshadow with a brush dipped in water, eye crayons, lip pencils or lipstick and a brush. It might be easier if you get a mate to help with this.

6. Add flowers to your hair. We pushed Leanne's hair off her face with a zig-zag band and pushed some flower hairclips in front.

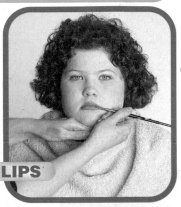

LIPS

FLOWERS

HAIR

113

CONTINUED OVER

Stephanie and Leanne are all set for summer.

Leanne

We added some silver eyeshadow to the centre of the eyelids and blended it into the pink. A little silver eyeliner was also smudged under Leanne's lower lashes. You can add an extra coat of mascara for night-time. Leanne's lipstick was changed to a deeper pink and clear gloss made it sparkle. Stick some sequins to the centre of your flowers.

Clothes:
Pink striped jumper, *Bhs.* Pink glitter zig-zag band and shiny daisy hairclips, *Tammy.*
Pink striped T-shirt, *C&A.* Narrow hairbands (set of 3), *Tammy.*

go for it!

Add some extra shimmer 'n' shine for a summer disco.

Stephanie

The lilac on Stephanie's eyes was changed to an ocean coloured turquoise and taken right up to the brows. A little seashell white was used to highlight the centre of the eyelids and sky blue was blended in at the outer corners and under the lower lashes. Lipstick was changed to pale pink and silver gloss finished the look.

Stephanie's hair was simply given a centre parting and two sections at the front were held with shiny blue daisy clips (to match the daisy trim on her dress).

Clothes:
Dress and hairclips, *Tammy.*
T-shirt, *Bhs.*

114

The zig-zag band was left in Leanne's hair, but the front section was parted in the middle and held with shiny pink clips.

Clothes:
Crochet top and flower necklace, *C&A.*
Pink and silver striped top, *Tammy.*
Hairclips, *New Look.*

flower Power

Let flowers spread to your whole outfit! All these clothes are from Tammy.

To do a hairstyle like this, pull your hair back into a low pony tail. Twist it up and secure with a large hairclip at the top of your head. Fluff out the ends and hold in place with hairspray. We put some sparkly hairclips in at the front, too. These added a bit of extra colour.

The Ice Girls

MARIANNE LUKE (aged 4)
I come on Saturday mornings to the Polar Bear Club — it's good fun. I have three badges and for my next badge I have to skate backwards.

ICE-SKATING'S hotting up! Lots of girls are taking up this brilliant hobby and there are plans to start up training schools so Britain can produce world standard skaters in the next few years.

But you still have to start at the bottom (ouch!), so we went along to Whitley Bay Ice Rink to get all the goss. Remember these girls' names —there could be a future Olympic star here!

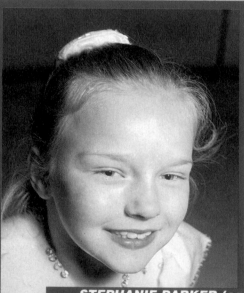

FAYE WINTLE (aged 14)
Training takes up most of my time, so I do miss hanging out with my mates. But I LOVE skating and the thought of one day being a champion makes it all worthwhile!

STEPHANIE PARKER (aged 8)
My mum's a coach so I've been skating since I was very small. I have seven badges, but I really just like skating for fun.

SOPHIE WATSON (aged 7)
I've been skating longer than I can remember! I have all twelve badges and skate four days a week. My fave skater is Tara Lipinski.

VICTORIA CHATTERTON (aged 8)
I come here two or three times a week and have ten badges — only two more to go! My ambition is to skate in the Olympics!

EVIE SENIOR (aged 5)
I'm in Class 3 in the Polar Bear Club. Jade gave me this Mickey Mouse dress when she grew out of it. Her mum made it.

JADE BROWN (aged 8)
After the Polar Bear Club, you go on to the National Ice Skating Association tests. I've got the first one which is called Novice. My mum designs all my lovely dresses.

FAY BRINDLE (aged 14)
I'm looking forward to my first competition, which is the British Novice Championship. It's marked just like the Olympics with a maximum of 6.0. Part of the competition is looking good, so I have my dresses specially made.

So, interested in taking up ice skating? Why not go along to your local ice rink and join the Skating Club? Then you can start earning your badges or just have fun!

117

LOUISE

It's A

OCTOBER

S		3	10	17	24	31
M		4	11	18	25	—
Tu		5	12	19	26	—
W		6	13	20	27	—
Th		7	14	21	28	—
F	1	8	15	22	29	—
S	2	9	16	23	30	—

IMPORTANT DATES!

Keith Duffy (Boyzone) — *1st*
Kevin Richardson (Backstreet Boys) — *3rd*
Shaznay Lewis (All Saints) — *14th*
Dannii Minogue — *20th*
Zac Hanson — *22nd*
British Summertime ends/ clocks go back — *24th*
Lee Brennan — *27th*
Winona Ryder — *29th*
Hallowe'en — *31st*

WRITE ON!

Hollyoaks
c/o Merseyside TV
Campus Manor
Childwall
Abbey Road
Liverpool
L16 4JF

Paul Nicholls
P.O. Box 2660
Brighton
BN1 1SX

No Doubt
c/o MCA Records
139 Piccadilly
London
W1V 0AX

Louise
P.O. Box 888
High Wycombe
Bucks
HP11 2NY

WINONA RYDER

Date!

NOVEMBER

S	–	7	14	21	28
M	1	8	15	22	29
Tu	2	9	16	23	30
W	3	10	17	24	–
Th	4	11	18	25	–
F	5	12	19	26	–
S	6	13	20	27	–

ZOË BALL

WRITE ON!

North And South
Freepost SW8031
P.O. Box 607
London
SW6 4YY

OTT
2 Carriglea
Naas Road
Dublin

Mark Owen
P.O. Box 5405
London
W7 1ZT

Will Smith
Creative Artists
9830 Wilshire
Boulevard
Beverly Hills
CA 90212
USA

IMPORTANT DATES!

Louise Nurding — 4th
Kavana — 4th
Guy Fawkes Night — 5th
Leonardo DiCaprio — 11th
**David Schwimmer
(Friends) — 12th**
Bjork — 12th
Remembrance Sunday — 14th
Isaac Hanson — 17th
Ant McPartlin — 18th
Alex James (Blur) — 21st
Zoë Ball — 23rd
Ryan Giggs
(Manchester United) — 29th
**Alan Fitzsimons
(OTT) — 29th**
St Andrew's Day — 30th

DAVID SCHWIMMER

119

It's A Date!

IMPORTANT DATES!

Anna Chlumsky (My Girl) — 3rd
Aaron Carter — 7th
Teri Hatcher
(Lois in Superman) — 8th
Easther Bennett (Eternal) — 11th
Brad Pitt — 18th
Jamie Theakston — 21st
Paul Byatt (Mike Dixon in
Brookside) — 22nd
Nicole Appleton (All Saints) — 23rd
Christmas Eve — 24th
Christmas Day — 25th
Boxing Day — 26th
New Year's Eve — 31st

WRITE ON!

Spice Girls
Freepost
P.O. Box 859
London
SW11 4BR

Party Of Five
c/o High Road
Productions
10202 West
Washington Boulevard
Culver City
CA 90232
USA

Brad Pitt
c/o Triad Artists
10100 Santa Monica
Boulevard
Suite 505
CA 90067
USA

Oasis
Mailing Service
Freepost CV744
3 Alveston Place
Leamington Spa
CV32 4BR

DECEMBER

S	–	5	12	19	26
M	–	6	13	20	27
Tu	–	7	14	21	28
W	1	8	15	22	29
Th	2	9	16	23	30
F	3	10	17	24	31
S	4	11	18	25	–

ALL SAINTS

SPICE GIRLS

AARON CARTER

120

121

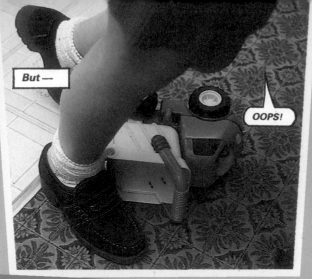

122

Wildlife
SUMATRAN TIGERS

MORE Model